THE COMPLEMENTARY HEALTH GUIDE

The Complementary Health Guide   Second Edition
Copyright © 1993
Edited by Amanda Chambers
Published by English Countryside Publications
Advertising: Prowse & Saunders
The Studio Centre, Wiston Road
Nayland, Colchester, Essex CO6 4LT
Telephone: 0206 262262
Origination: Anglia Photoset Ltd, Colchester
Distribution: MLP Limited, Market Link House, Tye Green,
Elsenham, Bishops Stortford, Herts CM22 6DY
Telephone: 0279 647555

Printed in G.B.   I.S.B.N. 1 870112 19 9

Foreword

By Michael Endacott

Complementary Medicine is Holism in Practice

The past year has been one of significant progress in all areas of complementary medicine. More people than ever before are looking towards new forms of healing to help overcome chronic conditions. The media have helped by presenting a continuous stream of articles purporting to show how and when the disciplines/therapies can work. For good balance, there has also been a sprinkling which offer a critical view. This is no bad thing.

Too often do we hear "complementary medicine is harmless, non-toxic and non-invasive" when, in reality, the reverse can be the truth. All these forms of health care have an effect on the physical, mental, emotional and vital energy levels of human consciousness. The effect can either be a positive reaction designed to help the patient to regain full health and vitality or a negative reaction where nothing at all appears to happen.

Damage can occur when unskilled practitioners in any area are unaware of the efficacy of their therapy and use techniques incorrectly. This is usually because they have had insufficient training and cannot recognise danger areas.

Patients sometimes consider the "healing crisis" or the increase of symptoms which follow treatment as a negative response whilst the reverse is true. The changes which are occurring are nature's way of throwing off the symptoms in order to re-establish normality.

These changes can be alarming. The qualified practitioner will always warn of these possibilities. Once the patient knows what to expect, the anxiety is removed and progress made. However, these dramatic changes are the exception rather than the rule. Nature is kind to us and usually allows healing to take place gradually and at a pace which the patient can accept.

It is this gradual process which can cause irritation because society has grown to expect immediate change. Patients forget it has often taken months – even years – for the condition to manifest in the body and it may well take a similar time to be overcome. Take a pill and the pain is eased; try complementary medicine and the cause of the problem is addressed. A cure will usually take time.

The current popularity of complementary medicine is undoubtedly due to its effectiveness. People try it and get better. What more wonderful compliment to the practitioners?

However, there are a number of problems which must be overcome if we are to see the development of complementary medicine continued into the twenty-first century. Practitioners usually share a number of attributes of character and skill which can place them in a position of insecurity.

Humility and deep dedication to helping mankind does not sit well with demanding correct fee structures. Too many patients try to get treatment for nothing. Poverty is always a problem, but our first concern must be to ensure that NHS funds are made available to cover complementary medicine.

Most practitioners know that their abilities are

akin to a gift from God, although they have had to study many years in order to perfect their skill and to understand the philosophy of their specialism.

Until recently, training in complementary medicine has been a hit or miss affair. The advent of the EEC and the requirements of the National Council of Vocational Qualifications (NCVQ) have brought a new urgency to registration. At present there is no national standard of training although some disciplines are moving to formal qualifications. This is to be welcomed. The NCVQ approach is to allow practitioners to get credit for the skills which they can show they possess. This is entirely fair and will ensure that years of practitioner experience are not ignored because there is no special piece of paper on the wall.

Most practitioners are safe and effective but the public and the Authorities must be certain that all practitioners are aware of contra-indications, differential diagnosis, practice management, philosophical knowledge and clinical practice before they will recognise them.

Practitioner insurance and Codes of Conduct and Ethics are not standard although much has been done by individual groups to regularise their members' position and to ensure public safety. Practitioners now follow the ICM lead and seek to "complement" the needs of the patient at physical mental and spiritual levels.

The problems are mainly a question of terminology. When is a practitioner not a practitioner? When s/he is a therapist. When is a Beauty Therapist not a Beauty Therapist? When s/he is a Clinical Practitioner. What is the difference between a medical diagnosis and a health assessment? Answer – None! They are both the same.

The Beauty Industry has provided a remarkable service for many years and done much to pioneer the promotion of various forms of complementary medicine. However, we now find people offering a very limited range of skills under the general therapy title. This can serve to devalue the work of the skilled practitioners. In aromatherapy, it is possible for a hairdresser to qualify to offer relaxation using five essential oils. A beauty therapist will be qualified to use over 60 oils and treat a number of specific conditions. The practitioner will be qualified to use over 120 oils and be able to treat health conditions. All are called aromatherapists but the public has no means of knowing how to recognise the different levels of skill and competence.

In Europe the word "therapist" tends to be used to describe those who work under supervision whereas the "practitioner" will work as an independent specialist. This is why we have created the British Register of Complementary Practitioners.

Some complementary organisations have written their constitutions in such a way as to remove the right of their members to make a "medical diagnosis". It is clear that a complementary practitioner who is not a qualified doctor will be unable to diagnose in the same way as a GP, but that does not mean that he cannot offer a valuable contribution from within his own specialist terms of reference. The aromatherapist will diagnose which oils to use and in which order; the acupuncturist will diagnose in which points to insert the needles; the hypnotherapist will diagnose whether or not to treat the patient and which techniques are most appropriate, and so on through all the disciplines.

These arguments may appear as "splitting hairs" but are essential if the freedom of choice at present enjoyed by the general public is to be maintained. The patient needs to be able to take some decisions with regard to the best possible treatment and this can only be done if he is well informed. Patients now question their doctors on the advisability of complementary medicine. Doctors are more open in their appreciation of these techniques. Indeed, many G.P.s now employ complementary practitioners or refer to local clinics.

Even in this enlightened atmosphere, we have to be careful of limiting legislation advancing quietly through the back door. The Consumer Protection Regulation due from Brussels in 1993 will change the methods of procedure in making a complaint about services. Hitherto, the recipient has had to prove that damage has been done to them. In future the provider will have to prove that they did not do the damage or could not have foreseen it. A complete reversal which will affect all service industries including complementary medicine.

In the Autumn of 1991, the Minister of Health, Stephen Dorrell, announced that in future doctors would "delegate" patients to complementary practitioners. This would leave the doctor in overall charge of the patient, but might also be used as an excuse to demand that every patient MUST consult a doctor BEFORE consulting a complementary practitioner. This can be seen as an attempt to limit private practice and an interference with the freedom of public choice.

All this detail will give the reader a background to some of the current developments in complementary medicine. However, in every discipline and therapy there is progress towards national registration and the creation of practice standards.

At a seminar organised by the British Register of Complementary Practitioners in September 1992 to consider accreditation in complementary medicine, 475 organisations were represented. This shows the extent of the desire for professionalism and the willingness to co-operate in all areas. The Consultant from the National Council of Vocational Qualifications confirmed that the Institute for Complementary Medicine and the British Register were providing the correct structure for NCVQ accreditation in the future. It was also mentioned that the ICM is the only organisation working in this way.

How To Use This Directory

The problem with this directory (and with any other similar listing) is that there is no way to discover the depth and quality of practitioner skills. Membership of most registers is usually based on "in house" assessment without external validation or accreditation. Insurance has been obtained relatively easily, although the major companies are looking to tighten entry requirements.

1. You can check on qualifications by contacting the ICM. They may be able to give you some factual data but not opinions.

2. If the practitioner is local, speak to him and ask if he can help your condition. Also ask for the scale of fees and other details of the practice. Is the practitioner well known and with a good reputation?

3. Do not commit yourself to more than one session/treatment until you have made your own assessment of the practitioner.

a. Was the receptionist helpful and approachable?

b. Were you treated courteously and correctly?

c. Were you seen on time? If not, were you given a reason for the delay?

d. Did the practitioner spend time asking questions? Did s/he appear to understand your problem?
e. Did you feel a sense of confidence in the practitioner.

4. Even if you have a positive feeling, do not sign up for an unlimited number of treatments. See how you progress.

If you are receiving treatment from your doctor, tell him what you propose. Under no circumstances give up your medication without consulting your doctor first. Some practitioners say they cannot treat if medication is still being taken. In this case be extra careful. Do take matters slowly and try to play an active part in your treatment. Co-operate with the practitioner and ask questions. Make sure that you receive satisfactory answers.

Healing will take place in your physical, mental, emotional and vital energy levels so cultivate a quiet confidence that you are getting better.

In some cases it may be necessary to have more than one therapy as you overcome the symptoms. Please be cautious about doing more than one treatment at a time and ask your original practitioner to advise.

All this background information will help to ensure that the individual patient receives the treatment needed to help to restore health and vitality. The major anxiety is that complementary practitioners will not spot potential illness and life-threatening conditions will go unnoticed and untreated. This is why it is important for the complementary practitioner to have had a full training and enjoy a correct professional relationship with the patient's medical doctor.

National registration, accreditation and validation are all in the process of development. As the leading facilitating body, the ICM sees its duty as providing every practitioner with credits for the skills which they possess and having them recorded on a national and international basis.

In again being invited to write the foreword for this Directory, I must ask all readers to use common sense and exercise caution. However, the ICM survey of 1983 suggested that 75 per cent of all new clients had been referred by satisfied patients and there is every reason to believe that the record is the same today. May each reader find the healing that they need.

Michael Endacott,
Deputy Director
Institute for Complementary Medicine
PO Box 194
London SE16 1QZ.

About the front cover . . .

"This painting is one of a series relating to the very old, powerful, brooding, and beautiful hills near Brechfa in West Wales, where for some years Daphne and I lived, seventeen miles from a supermarket and one and a half miles from a small village.

It also relates to a wonderful experience – some four years ago two friends came for Christmas; sleeping in a wooden chalet in the woods near our cottage.

At about half past one on the night of Christmas eve we crept up to the chalet in the dark to leave a present; jingling bells, playing Christmas tunes and trying not to giggle! But, as we returned everything changed – awe, deep happiness and quiet energy came to us and we knew that we were taking part in celebrations that had gone on around these hills, in some form, for thousands of years."

Eddie Franklin, Studio 8, La Berlingotte Chateau 71250 Cluny, France

Acknowledgements

The Publishers would like to thank all contributors who advised and assisted in the publication of this book.

Contents

Index of Professional Qualifications/ and Common Abbreviations

ABATH	Associate British Association of Therapeutical Hypnotists
ABHA	Associate British Hypnotherapy Association
ABMAcS	Associate British Medical Acupuncture Society
ABT	Association of Bodymind Therapists
ACOH	Associate of the College of Healing
AIIVMT	Associate of the International Institute of Vitamin and Mineral Therapists
AIRMT	Associate of the International Register of Manipulative Therapists
AMA	Anthroposophical Medical Association
AMP	Association of Massage Practitioners
ANLP	Association for NLP
APMT(GB)	Associate of Professional Music Therapists in Great Britain
ASBTh	Associate of Society of Health and Beauty Therapists
ATA	Association of Tisserand Aromatherapists
ATAcS	Associate Traditional Acupuncture Society
BAAR	British Acupuncture Association and Register
BAc	Bachelor of Acupuncture
BAHA	British Alliance of Healing Associations
BCA	British Chiropractic Association
BHMA	British Holistic Medical Association
BPsS	British Society of Psychotherapists
BRCP	British Register of Complementary Practitioners
BRS	British Rebirth Society
BSD	British Society of Dowsers
BWOY	British Wheel of Yoga
CAc	Certificate of Acupuncture (China)
CCAc	Certificate in Chinese Acupressure
CertHS	Certificate in Herbal Studies
CHP	Certificate in Hypnotherapy and Psychotherapy (National College of Hypnosis and Psychotherapy)
CHyp	Certified Hypnotherapist (Member of the British Council of Hypnotist Examiners)
CHyp	Council of Hypnotherapies
CMH	Certified Master Hypnotist (Member of the British Council of Hypnotist Examiners)
DAc	Diploma in Acupuncture (College of Traditional Chinese Acupuncture)
DC	Diploma in Chiropractic
DHM	Diploma in Holistic Medicine
DHom	Diploma in Homoeopathy
DHP	Diploma in Hypnotherapy and Psychotherapy (National College of Hypnotherapy and Psychotherapy)
DHyp	Diploma Hypnotherapist (The Proudfoot School of Hypnosis)
DipBWY	British Wheel of Yoga Diploma
DipC	Diploma in Counselling
DipHyp	Diploma in Hypnotherapy
DipMSCT	Diploma of the Mercurian School
DipPC	Diploma in Psychic Counselling
DipPhyt	Diploma in Phytotherapy (herbal medicine)
DipTHP	Diploma in Therapeutic Hypnosis & Psychotherapy
DMH	Diploma Master Hypnotist (Proudfoot School of Hypnosis)
DO	Diploma in Osteopathy
DrAc	Doctor of Acupuncture (British College of Acupuncture)
DSH	Diploma from the School of Homoeopathy
DSNU	Diploma of Spiritualist National Union
DThD	Diploma in Dietary Therapy
DTM	Diploma in Therapeutic Massage (London College of Holistic Medicine)
FBAcA	Fellow of the British Acupuncture Association
FBABThC	Fellow of the British Association of Beauty Therapy and Cosmetology
FBATH	Fellow of the British Association of Therapeutical Hypnotists
FBCHP	Fellow of the British Clinic of Hypnotherapy and Psychotherapy
FBHA	Fellow of the British Hypnotherapy Association
FBHU	Fellow of the British Herbal Union
FBPsS	Fellow British Psychological Society
FBRA	Fellow of the British Reflexology Association
FCO	Fellow of the College of Osteopaths
FCOH	Fellow of the College of Healing
FFHom	Fellow of the Faculty of Homoeopathy
FIIVMT	Fellow of the International Institute of Vitamin and Mineral Therapists
FIPM	Fellow of the Institute of Psionic Medicine
FIPTI	Fellow Independent Professional Therapists International
FLCO	Fellow of the London College of Osteopaths
FNIMH	Fellow of the National Institute of Medical Herbalists
FPPTh	The Faculty of Professional Practising Therapies
FRadA	Fellow of the Radionics Association
FRH	Fellow of the Register of Herbalists
FSBTh	Fellow of the Society of Health and Beauty Therapists
FTAcS	Fellow of the Traditional Acupuncture Society
IRNHP	Independent Register of Natural health Practitioners
ISPA	International Society of Practising Aromatherapists

LCCH	London College of Classical Homoeopathy	MGPMP	Member of the Guild of Professional Massage Practitioners
LCH	Licentiate of the College of Homoeopathy		
LCHom	Licentiate of the College of Homoeopaths	MH	Master Herbalist
LCSP	London and Counties Society of Physiologists	MHPA	Member of the Health Practitioners Association
LCSP(Assoc)	Associate of the London Counties Society of Physiologists (awarded after completion of the course in Remedial (Swedish) Massage)	MIACT	Member of the International Association of Colour Therapists
		MIAH	Member of the Institute of Analytical Hypnotherapists
LCSP(Bth)	Full Member of LCSP (Beauty Therapy)		
LCSP(Chir)	Full member of LCSP (Chiropody)	MIAO	Member of the Institute of Applied Osteopathy
LCSP(Phys)	Full member of LCSP (Remedial Massage and Manipulative Therapy)	MICH	Member of the Institute of Curative Hypnotherapists
LicAc	Licentiate in Acupuncture	MICR	Member of the International College of Radionics
LicAc(AWA)	Licentiate of the Academy of Western Acupuncture (medically qualified – doctors, dentists, nurses)	MIFA	Member of the International Federation of Aromatherapists
		MIGN(med)	Member of the International Guild of Natural Medicine Practitioners
LLSA	Licentiate of the London School of Aromatherapy		
LNCP	Licentiate of National Council of Psychotherapists	MIIR	Member of the International Institute of Reflexology
MAA	Member of the Auricular Therapy Association	MInstAT	Member of the Institute of Allergy Therapists
MAc	Master of Acupuncture	MIPC	Member of the Institute of Pure Chiropractic
MACH	Member of the Association of Classical Hypnotherapists	MIPM	Member of the Institute of Psionic Medicine (Psionic Medical Society)
MAEPH	Member of the Association of Ethical and Professional Hynpotherapists	MIPTI	Member of the Independent Professional Therapists International
MAPT	Member of Association of Professional Therapists	MIRMT	Member of the Independent Register of Manipulative Therapists
MAQCH	Member of the Association of Qualified Curative Hypnotherapists	MIROM	Member of the International Register of Oriental Medicine
MAR	Member of the Association of Reflexologists		
MAWAc	Member of the Association of Western Acupuncture	MISPH	Member of the International Society for Professional Hypnosis
MBAcA	Member of the British Acupuncture Association	MISPT	Member of the International Society of Polarity Therapists
MBEOA	Member of the British European Osteopathic Association		
		MLCO	Member of the London College of Osteopathic Medicine
MBNOA	Member of the British Naturopathic and Osteopathic Association		
		MMSM	Member of the Midlands School of Massage
MBRA	Member of the British Reflexology Association	MNAHP	Member of the National Association of Hypnotists and Psychotherapists
MBRI	Member of the British Register of Iridologists		
MBSAM	Member of the British School of Acupressure	MNCPHR	Member of the National Council of Psychotherapists and Hypnotherapy Register
MBSH	Member of the British Society of Hypnotherapists		
MBSR	Member of the British School of Reflexology	MNIMH	Member of the National Institute of Medical Herbalists
MC	McTimoney Chiropractor		
MCH	Member of the College of Homeopathy	MNPCHR	Member of the National Council of Psychotherapists and Hypnotherapists Register
MCO	Member of the College of Osteopaths		
MCOA	Member of the Cranial Osteopath Association	MNTOS	Member of the Natural Therapeutic and Osteopathic Society
MCOH	Member of the College of Healing		
MCROA	Member of the Cranial Osteopathic Association	MPNLP	NLP Master Practitioner
MDH	Indian homoeopathic qualification	MRadA	Member of the Radionics Association
MFG	Member of the Feldenkrais Guild	MRCHM	Member of the Register of Chinese Herbal Medicine
MFHom	Member of the Faculty of Homoeopathy		
MGNM	Member of the Guild of Natural Medicine Practitioners	MRCMT	Member of the Register of Chinese Massage Therapy
MGNMed	Member of the Guild of Natural Medicine Practitioners (covers various qualifications and diplomas)	MRCN	Member of the Register of Clinical Nutritionists
		MRH	Member of the Register of Herbalists
		MRN	Member of the General Council and Register of Naturopaths
MGO	Member of the Guild of Osteopathy		

MRO	Member of the Register of Osteopaths		**ND**	Diploma in Naturopathy
MRSS	Member of the Register of the Shiatsu Society		**NFSH**	National Federation of Spiritual Healers
MRTCM	Member of the Register of Traditional Chinese Medicine		**NRHP**	National Register of Hypnotherapists and Psychotherapists
MSAA	Member of the Society of Auricular Acupuncturists		**RIr**	Registered Iridologist
MSAPP	Member of the Society of Advanced Psychotherapists and Parapsychologists		**RMANM**	Registered Member of the Association of Natural Medicines
MSBTh	Member of the Society of Health and Beauty Therapists		**RMAPC**	Registered Member of the Association of Psychic Counsellors
MSHP	Member of the Society of Holistic Practitioners		**RNTOS**	Register of the Natural Therapeutic and Osteopathic Society
MSO	Member of the Society of Osteopaths (European School of Osteopathy)		**RPT**	Registered Polarity Therapist
MSS	Member of Shiatsu Society		**RSHom**	Registered with the Society of Homoeopaths
MSTAT	Member of the Society of Teachers of the Alexander Technique		**RTCM**	Register of Traditional Chinese Medicine
			SAPP	Society of Advanced Psychotherapy Practitioners
MTAcs	Member of the Traditional Acupuncture Society		**SMD**	Swedish Massage Diploma
MWFH	Member of the World Federation of Hypnotherapists		**TDHA**	Tisserand Diploma in Holistic Aromatherapy

---

For additional information on a particular therapy and a list of practitioners, contact the Society or Association listed beneath the relevant synopsis.

The following organisations offer a wealth of information and advice including training standards on a wide range of therapies.

It is always advisable to enclose an SAE with any enquiry.

The Institute for Complementary Medicine,
P.O. Box 194, London SE16 1QZ.

The Natural Health Network,
Chardstock House, Chard, Somerset TA20 2TL.
Tel: 04606 3229.

The National Consultative Council,
(Enquiries to John Hopson), 39 Prestbury Road,
Cheltenham, Gloucestershire GL52 9PT.
Tel: 0242 512601.

Council for Complementary Medicine,
10 Belgrave Square, London SW1 8PU.

The British Holistic Medical Association,
179 Gloucester Place, London NW1 6DX.
Tel: 071-262 5299.

ACUPRESSURE

Acupressure can be called "acupuncture without needles". Acupressure works by stimulating the points with the help of pressure from the fingers and the thumbs.

Apparent advantages of acupressure are:
1. Though simple and easy, acupressure is an effective treatment.
2 A person can treat himself in the privacy of his or her own home.
3. The treatment may be taken as often as is needed.
4. Acupressure treatment is completely free from side-effects.

Acupressure is a self treatment and compels every person to take an interest in his or her own health. Health can be maintained easily by taking a regular treatment of acupressure points every day. A short acupressure session in the morning helps to maintain the balance of energy flowing through the body. This leads to the prevention of disease. Prevention is not only better than cure but also cheaper.

Acupressure helps to increase vitality and strength. Pressure is applied to points to cure illness, pain or create an anaesthetic effect. Acupressure is very helpful for any stress related symptoms and in addition to this it helps to decrease stiffness, PMT, asthma, headaches, insomnia, back pain, digestion problems, poor circulation and allergies.

T. H. Jivraj, B.Sc., D.Hom.(Med.)
D.Acupressure, Cert. in Counselling
Natural Health Clinic
286 Preston Road, Harrow
Middlesex HA3 0QA
Tel: 081-908 4272

The European Shiatsu School   0672 86362

LONDON

West London School of Therapeutic
Massage   071-229 4672

SURREY

Barry McManus, B.Sc., R.N.H.P.Dip., A.P.N.T., M.I.F.A.,
10, Benhilton Gardens, Sutton, Surrey   **081-641-4525**

YORKSHIRE

Enrico Dodson, L.C.S.P.(Assoc.), M.I.I.R., M.B.S.A.M.,
21 Cowlersley Lane, Huddersfield HD4 5TY   **0484 641982**

ACUPUNCTURE
(SEE ALSO CHINESE TRADITIONAL MEDICINE)

Acupuncture is an ancient system of healing. The earliest acupuncture books were written 4,500 years ago and today, world-wide, there are over three million practitioners.

Acupuncture began with the discovery that the stimulation of specific areas of the skin affected the functioning of certain organs of the body. It evolved into a system of healing as the connection between the skin and the organs was better understood and more sensitive ways of stimulation were devised.

In the West, acupuncture has been misleadingly publicised as only being helpful in specific conditions, for example, pain or weight loss; whereas, in fact, it is extremely effective in a wide variety of conditions through its power to stimulate our own healing responses. This overall therapeutic effect is one of its great strengths.

Traditional Acupuncture Society
1 The Ridgeway, Stratford-upon-Avon
Warwickshire CV37 9JL
Tel: 0789 298798

British Acupuncture Association and Register
34 Alderney Street, London SW1V 4EU
Tel: 071-834 1012

British College of Acupuncture
8 Hunter Street, London WC1N 1BN
Tel: 071-833 8164

Council for Acupuncture
179 Gloucester Place, London NW1 6DX
Tel: 071-724 5756

DERBYSHIRE

Martin Harvey, B.A., M.R.T.C.M., Natural Choice Therapy Centre, 24 St
John Street, Ashbourne, Derbyshire DE6 1GH   0335 46096

DEVON

Talal Amin, Dp.Ac.M.R.T.C.M., Acupuncturist, Acupuncture realines and balances, the body's own energies to resolve disease and achieve health and vitality (0884) 255990

ESSEX

Jenny Lovell, Lic.Ac., M.T.A.S.   0206 764083
or 0206 561150

ACUPUNCTURE

GLOUCESTER

The Acupuncture Clinic
Kemerton, Nr. Tewkesbury, Glos. GL20 7HX
Tel: 038 689 461
Open: Monday – Friday
Meriel Darby, M.Ac., M.T.A.S.,
Linda Holmes, Lic.Ac., M.T.A.S.,
Tom Jennings, M.Ac., M.T.A.S.

HAMPSHIRE

Traditional Acupuncture, at The Southsea Centre for Complementary Medicine 0705 874748
See our ad under Health Centres

HERTFORDSHIRE

Margaret Izod, M.D.M.A. Acupuncture, Homoeopathy, Reflexology, Bach Flower, 44a High Street, Hoddesdon, Herts EN11 8DA **0992 443462 or 0279 651063**

INVERNESS

Claire Gant, Lic.Ac.
Practitioner of Traditional Chinese Acupuncture

Inverness Natural
Therapy Centre
7 View Place, Inverness
0463 711 060

14 Forsyth Place
Cromarty
Rosshire
0381 7545

LONDON

Acupuncture and Osteopathic Centre
34 Alderney Street, London SW1V 4EU

Telephone: 071-834 6229/1012

Rosemarie Anderson, Lic.Ac., M.T.A.S.
3A Sheen Gate Gardens, London SW14 7PD
Tel: 081-876 7960
Aims of traditional acupuncture:
1. to release the symptom through understanding
2. thereby nurturing the character
3. thereby helping the patient to reach full potential

Teresa Barlow, Acupuncturist, B.Sc., M.I.R.O.M., L.C.S.P., The South London Natural Health Centre **071-720 8817**

Atsuko Cowley, Acupuncturist, M.I.R.O.M., The South London Natural Health Centre **071-720 8817**

Micheal Weiland, B.Ac., M.I.R.O.M., The South London Natural Health Centre **071-720 8817**

Heather Algar, B.A., Lic.Ac.
Member of The Traditional Acupuncture Society.
ACUPUNCTURE combined with therapeutic massage, giving effective treatment for many stress related problems.
Telephone (Hampstead) 071 483 2156

The Chinese Medicine Clinic, Muswell Hill N10. Chinese Herbal Medicine, Chinese Clinical Massage Therapy, Acupuncture **081-444 0103**

LOTHIAN

Jim Welsh, Dip.AC., R.T.C.M., Dip.T.M.,
Therapeutic Massage **031-551 5091**

ACUPUNCTURE

MERSEYSIDE

H. Simpson, D.O.-N.C.S.O., M.G.O.(Lon), M.I.C.A.K., M.R.S.H., M.H.P.A., M.A.A., M.C.K.O.R.E.   **0744 88 3737**

SOMERSET

Complementary Medicine Centre, 9 Corporation Street, Taunton, Somerset TA1 4AJ   **0823 325022**
or Redgate Medical Centre, Westonsoyland, Bridgwater, Somerset TA6 5BF   **0278 444411**

SURREY

Farnham Holistic Centre, Tilford Road, Farnham, Surrey GU9 8HU   **0252 734445**

SUSSEX

The Floatarium, 21 Bond Street, Brighton BN1 1RD   **0273 679555**
Fax 0273 601 992

AIKIDO

Aikido – <u>The way of Spiritual Harmony</u> – is a Japanese system of self-defence that provides an excellent basis for both physical and spiritual development. Essentially non-violent and in its orthodox form non-competitive, it is not based on striking or kicking but on skilful body movement. Not requiring physical strength or aggressive spirit it can be practised by men and women of all ages. Aikido exercises every portion of the body. Flexibility, co-ordination, balance and quick reaction are all developed.

In common with other Oriental philosophies, Aikido teaches that there is no real separation between that which is body and that which is mind. Thus in subjecting our bodies to the precise discipline of Aikido we may steadily influence our minds for the good: creating an inner calm and balance that will be carried into our daily lives, helping us to become better and more effective people.

For information about centres of Aikido teaching throughout the country contact:

General Secretary
The British Aikido Federation
Yew Tree Cottage, Toot Baldon
Oxford OX44 9NE
Tel: 086 738 500

THE ALEXANDER TECHNIQUE

The Alexander Technique provides a practical means for change by bringing about an improvement in our balance and coordination.

Most people when they start having Alexander lessons are unaware of the fact that they distort their own framework through their own habitual thought processes. This distortion can give rise to a wide variety of problems from aches, pains and strains to, for example, anxiety, feelings of inadequacy or hopelessness, lack of confidence, loss of old skills and difficulty in acquiring new ones.

During Alexander lessons the improvement in our balance and coordination is brought about by the Alexander teacher who works with his/her hands, whilst simultaneously explaining the principles of the technique, and giving instructions in how to maintain this improved state in all our everyday activities. As lessons progress, people become increasingly aware of what they have been doing to themselves and of how to maintain this new poise and balance so that this becomes a constant in their life.

Once we are able to consciously control something as fundamental as our own poise and balance we are then in with a chance of also being able to consciously control other aspects of our behaviour such as the way we react to other people. This then opens up many new doors, enabling us to grow and develop, and fulfil our true potential in life.

The Professional Association of Alexander Teachers
14 Kingsland, Jesmond
Newcastle-upon-Tyne NE2 3AL
Tel: 091-281 8032

ALEXANDER TECHNIQUE

The PROFESSIONAL ASSOCIATION OF ALEXANDER TEACHERS
P.A.A.T. has teachers of the
ALEXANDER TECHNIQUE
throughout the country and runs a
THREE YEAR TRAINING COURSE
in Birmingham
For details contact the secretary   Telephone: 091 281 8032

CUMBRIA

Alexander Teaching Network
For a list of qualified teachers of the Alexander Technique
P.O. Box 53, Kendal, Cumbria LA9 4UP

ESSEX

Alexander Technique East,
Trinity Centre, 21 Trinity St., Colchester, Essex   **0206 561150**

Steve Knowland, S.T.A.T.   **0728 747918 or 0206 561150**

KENT

Mrs Shirley Crawford, M.S.T.A.T.,
The Old School House, Ide Hill,
Sevenoaks, Kent TN14 6JT
Telephone: 0732 750246

LONDON

Alexander Technique (The) (London), Refia Sacks and Alan Mars, S.T.A.T.
individual lessons and Courses, Alexander Technique for
Voice, Singing, Communication Skills and Pregnancy,
Residentials. The Highbury Centre, 137 Grosvenor
Avenue, London N5 2NH.
Tel: 071-226 5805/1815

The Bloomsbury Alexander Centre, Bristol House, 80a
Southampton Row, London WC1   **071-404 5348**

Eve Corrin, S.T.A.T., B.A. Russian Hons., Dip.Ed., Alexander Technique
for stress management and inner spaciousness   **071-609 6697**

Anja Dashwood, Alexander Technique Teacher, I.T.E.C.,
S.P.A., H.S.T.A.T., The South London Natural Health
Centre   **071-720 8817**

David Glassman,
M.S.T.A.T., 26 Cleveland Gardens NW2 1DY   **081-455 1317**

Violet Hill Studios   **071-624 6101/081-458 5368**

OXFORD

Steven Cooper, M.S.T.A.T., 10 York Road, Headington,
Oxford OX3 8NW   **0865 65511**

SOMERSET

Complementary Medicine Centre, 9 Corporation Street,
Taunton, Somerset TA1   **0823 325022**

ALLERGY THERAPY

For over 2,000 years, it has been recognised that some people react badly to certain foods, dusts, pollens and fumes and become ill as a result. The classic allergic response can be seen in, for instance, hay fever, urticarial rashes, asthma and eczema.

The range of illnesses which may be caused by allergy is very wide indeed, e.g. persistent tiredness, migraine and depression. Many illnesses which have previously been thought to be "all in the mind" may be successfully treated.

Food allergies can be identified and treated by avoidance diets, many other allergens by skin scratch tests or laboratory blood test. Muscle testing and the Vega test have proved to be extremely effective. The therapist may use muscle testing to identify the suspected allergens, then prepare a course of desensitisation treatment designed to lead to steady improvement in health, both in the short and long term. This may take the form of specially homoeopathically potentised allergens taken in the form of drops by mouth.

Donald M. Harrison
The Institute of Allergy Therapists
Ffynnonwen, Llangwryfon
Aberystwyth, Dfyed SY23 4EY
Tel: 09747 376

Action Against Allergy
24–26 High Street, Hampton Hill
Middlesex TW12 (Information centre – mail only)

THE INSTITUTE OF ALLERGY THERAPISTS
The Institute maintains a Register of
Practitioners and will give advice on the
homoeopathic treatment of allergy and the
address of your nearest therapist,
on request.
Details from:
D. M. Harrison, BA (Hons), BSc, MRPharmS,
Ffynnonwen
Natural Therapy Centre,
Llangwyryfon, Aberystwyth,
Dyfed. SY23 4EY Tel: 09747 376

14

ANTHROPOSOPHICAL MEDICINE

Anthroposophical Medicine is an extension of orthodox medicine practised exclusively by conventionally qualified doctors. Through Anthroposophy – the study of man founded by Rudolf Steiner – it is possible to experience that the human being has a spiritual as well as a mental and physical constitution. How these elements inter-relate in health and illness gives a broad framework for therapeutic work.

Through a qualitative approach to the scientific study of natural substances, new medicines and pharmaceutical processes have been developed.

Artistic work – drawing, painting, eurythmy (movement) and sculpture have been developed within Anthroposophical Medicine for use therapeutically. New insights have also been given to nursing, hydrotherapy and massage.

Anthroposophical Medicine supports the patient's own healing processes and it is fundamental that illness is a meaningful part of human life. Treated in an appropriate way, it may give opportunities for positive change and for developing a new balance in life.

Further information and a list of doctors who are available for consultation is available from the Secretary at the address below:

**Anthroposophical Medical Association
Rudolf Steiner House
35 Park Road, London NW1 6XT**

GLOUCESTERSHIRE

Dr. A. A. Turner, M.B., B.S.   0451 31373

KENT

THE RAPHAEL MEDICAL CENTRE

Residential Anthroposophical Medical Clinic. Treatment by qualified medical physicians and therapists. 24 hour nursing care. BUPA / PPP participating clinic.

For details and appointments write or phone to:

**The Raphael Medical Centre,
Coldharbour Lane, Hildenborough,
Tonbridge, Kent TN11 9LE
Tel: 0732 833924 Fax: 0732 838883**

WEST SUSSEX

WORCESTERSHIRE

AROMATHERAPY

Aromatherapy is a fragrant holistic therapy which uses natural plant oils to promote positive health. These essential oils may be extracted from flowers, such as lavender, or even trees, such as rosewood, and have a variety of actions on the physical body and the emotional state. Some are soothing and calming for irritated tissues or anxious states of mind, others may be stimulating and enlivening for a sluggish circulation or depressed mood. In the hands of a skilled therapist aromatherapy can help people with conditions as diverse as arthritis, psoriasis, sinusitis, sleep problems, period pains, migraine and M.E.

In Britain aromatherapy has grown rapidly in popularity and has been quoted to be now the fifth most popular alternative therapy. British therapists generally apply essential oils through massage, and are frequently also trained in complementary skills such as counselling, reflexology and nutrition. Fragrancing the air with burners or vaporisers and adding a few drops of oil to the bath are further ways to support aromatherapy treatments.

The Aromatherapy Organisations Council (AOC) has established a minimum of 180 class hours for training, to be introduced in all its associated training establishments by January 1994. This is to include 80 hours of aromatherapy, 60 hours of massage and 40 hours of anatomy and physiology.

Robert Tisserand
The Tisserand Institute, 65 Church Road
Hove, East Sussex BN3 2BD
Tel: 0273 206640

17

AROMATHERAPY

DERBYSHIRE

Alison Mold, B.Ed.(Hons), Dip.B.W.Y. (Cert. in Remedial Yoga) Dip.S.P.A., I.S.P.A. Natural Choice Therapy Centre, 24 St. John Street, Ashbourne, Derbyshire DE6 1GH. **0335 46096**

Edwina North, S.E.N., DoN, L.L.S.A., M.I.F.A. (Reg.) Natural Choice Therapy Centre, 24 St. John Street, Ashbourne, Derbyshire DE6 1GH **0335 46096**

DEVON

Rosalind Lacey, I.T.E.C., Qualified Therapist, Aromatherapy combined with remedial therapeutic massage. Contact the Clinic, 37 St Peter St, Tiverton **0884 255990**

ESSEX

Susan Ager, R.M.A.N.M., Aromatherapy to bring relaxation, stress reduction and skin care. Balances the mind and body **0245 74010**

Great Clacton Natural Healing Centre, 6 St John's Road, Great Clacton, Essex **0255 436059**

Lezanne Harris, I.S.P.A. **0376 41103** or **0206 561150**

Pauline Shorey, Dip.A.P.M., I.T.E.C., A.I.P.T.I., Association Complementary Health, Sandleigh Road, Leigh **714862**

GLOUCESTER

Valerie Johnston Deas, I.T.E.C., L.T.Phys., M.I.P.T.I., offers a psycho-spiritual approach **0242 224283**

HAMPSHIRE

Alison Perrott, S.P.Dip.A., M.I.S.P.A., M.I.S.M.A., M.A.S.K., M.T.M.I., The S.E.E.D. Institute, 10 Magnolia Way, Fleet, Hants GU13 9JZ **0252 626448**
See our ad under Courses & Tuition

HERTFORDSHIRE

Su Hagan, S.P.Dip.A., M.I.S.P.A., M.T.M.I., The S.E.E.D. Institute, Stable Flat, Serge Hill Road, Bedmond, Abbots Langley, Herts WD5 0RY **0923 268898**
See our ad under Courses & Tuition

KENT

LANCASHIRE

Mrs. Jolanta Basnyet,
B.A. (Hons), M.F.O., D.O., M.G.O.(Lon.), I.T.E.C., M.I.F.A., M.A.R.
Also practising Reflexology & Osteopathy
NATURAL HEALTH CENTRE
"Greenbank House", 65a Adelphi Street, Preston
Tel. 0772 825177

AROMATHERAPY

AROMATHERAPY

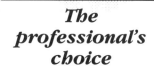

AROMATHERAPY

MIDDLESEX

SOMERSET

Complementary Medicine Centre, 9 Corporation Street,
Taunton, Somerset TA1 4AJ   0823 325022
or Redgate Medical Centre, Westonsoyland, Bridgwater,
Somerset TA6 5BF   0278 444411

June Markham, S.P.Dip.A., M.I.S.P.A., The S.E.E.D. Institute,
93A Ilchester Road, Yeovil, Somerset BA21 3BJ   0935 74379
See our Ad under Courses & Tuitions

SUFFOLK

Lynn Townsend James, I.T.E.C., M.F.Phys., I.P.T.I.,
Ancient House, Ellis Street, Boxford CO6 5HP   0787 211315

Lynda Noller, M.I.F.A., I.T.E.C., Brunswick, Moats Tye,
Stowmarket   0449 615351

Mrs. Margaret Weeds, M.I.F.A., M.B.S.R., S.P.A.Dip., M.I.P.T.I., I.T.E.C., 17
Freckenham Road, Worlington, Nr. Mildenhall, Suffolk IP28 8SQ.   0638 716759

SURREY

Monika E. Bloxwich, M.F.Phys., B.A.B.T.A.C., M.A.R.,
M.I.F.A.   071 730 8685 or 0293 785509

Farnham Holistic Centre, Tilford Road, Farnham, Surrey
GU9 8HU   0252 734445

Nigel Kettle, R.N.H.P.Dip., A.P.N.T., I.T.E.C., Sutton   081 641 4525

Barry McManus, B.Sc., R.N.H.P.Dip., A.P.N.T., M.I.F.A., 10 Benhilton
Gardens, Sutton, Surrey   081-641 4525

SUSSEX

Bay House Aromatics, 296a Ditchling Road, Brighton, East
Sussex, BN1 6JG   0273 559444. Fax: 0273 559444

The Floatarium, 21 Bond Street, Brighton
BN1 1RD   0273 679555 Fax: 0273 601 992

Visionary Designs, PO Box 1177, Brighton
BN1 1RX   0566 85243 Fax: 0566 85540

ART THERAPY

Therapy in Visual Art: Art Therapy and Artistic Therapy

Among the projective therapies, 'art therapy' or
'artistic therapy' has emerged as that special field of
therapy working principally with colour as in painting,
line as in drawing and form as in modelling.

The patient–client produces in art an external expression of an experience related to his or her own life, or
the clients participate in a process related to their lives.
Clients can experience in the art work – either consciously or by dimmest inkling or by change of breathing – references to their life situations which range
from feelings and thoughts to symbols or associations.

By continuing with the artistic process, they can
come to understand and atune the imbalances and
interrelationships within their own situation. The art
work itself – whether colour, form or line – has the
possibility even unconsciously to heal, just as in all
ages true works of art have had a healing capacity.

ART THERAPY

ART AND SELF DEVELOPMENT

Art and Self Development differs from Art Therapy in that the art work produced is seen as important in its own right. We are all naturally creative and allowing this to develop can lead to a build up of personal inner confidence.

Music, quietness, relaxation, guided meditation, gentle healing, laughter and a great variety of art work all play their part and there is sharing about the whole experience. Relevant techniques form a small but important part of the whole.

The 'right hand' brain is allowed to play its full part and we move towards the ideal of both sides of the brain playing their part. "I can", "It's OK for me to take note of my intuitive (highly efficient) self", "I matter."

Because the art work has its own value, activities can be a wonderful avenue of self development and can also be an introduction to further art work.

Art and Self Development activities can be for anyone and can benefit professional artists and designers just as well as people who have never painted.

Eddie Franklin
Studio 8, La Berlingotte
Chateau, 71250 Cluny
Tel: (010 33) 85 59 27 64

British Association of Art Therapists Ltd
11a Richmond Road, Brighton, BN2 3RL

Art and Self Development
Eddie Franklin runs weeks, weekends and fortnights in Wales, Somerset, London and France.
Brochure: **Hugh Davidson, Studio 8, 10 Wycliffe Row, Totterdown C, Bristol BS3 4RU. Tel: (0272) 713 488**

 TOBIAS SCHOOL OF ART

A three-year course leading to a diploma in Artistic Therapy. Weekend Workshops throughout the year.
Further details on Application

Tobias School of Art, Coombe Hill Road, East Grinstead, Sussex RH19 4LZ. Telephone (0342) 313655

ASTON PATTERNING

Aston Patterning was developed by Judith Aston as an integrated system of movement education, bodywork, environmental evaluation and fitness training designed to teach us how we can recover our body's natural unstressed fluidity and grace.

A former Professor of Dance and Movement for actors, dancers and athletes, she has worked with psychiatrists and their patients, helping to identify and modify patterns of behavioural expression, Aston trained with Dr. Rolf and developed a movement education system for Rolfing.

Aston Patterning recognises each person's unique body shape, asymmetries and limitations in a fluid understanding of the body's balance and sees all movement in terms of three dimensional spirals. The importance of our environment and good design or modification of chairs, shoes, beds, etc. is also taught.

The problem with most seating is that its shape encourages slouching and imposes compression in the body. When we try to move within a compressed posture; for instance whilst driving or sitting at a workstation, we add stress to the body. Judith Aston has designed a three piece wedge seat made of covered foam to modify any uncomfortable seating and bring it into line with the more conscious body. She lives in Mill Valley, California.

The Institute of Structural Bodywork
c/o Roger Golten, Synergy Centre
1 Cadogan Gardens, London SW3 2RJ

LONDON

Ingrid St Clare
Accredited Aston-Patterner.
Seminars and sessions.
Telephone 0536 725292

WILTSHIRE

ASHTANGA CENTRE
for
COMPLIMENTARY MEDICINE
Established in 1982. The Centre in addition to running training courses on **KINESIOLOGY, MASSAGE (ITEC) AND HYPNOSIS**, conducts a daily surgery in Trowbridge offering a wide range of therapies incl:
- **ALLERGY TESTING**
- **HYPNOSIS**
- **TOUCH FOR HEALTH (KINESIOLOGY)**
- **REFLEXOLOGY**
- **COUNSELLING (ONE TO ONE)**
The Centre also has for sale deep relaxation tapes to boost confidence and reduce stress. Also its very successful book bringing relief to arthritis suffers.
For a Private Confidential Consultation:
Telephone 0985 40659

ASTROLOGICAL COUNSELLING

The ancient art and science of Astrology has long been associated with health and holistic being. Many civilisations across the world use astrological information for assessing the causes of disease and to pinpoint methods of healing appropriate to each patient.

There are many ways in which the natal chart can help us to understand and alleviate the underlying energies that can cause disease. The emotions, thought patterns and belief systems of each person can be understood, often highlighting root causes of life-problems.

Many of the complementary therapies have strong correspondences with astrology – e.g. dietary supplements and Bach Flower Remedies. It has been linked with herbs since Culpepper in 1655 and with Ayurveda for hundreds of years before that.

A natal chart gives an opportunity to study an overview of the whole person, and can stand on its own or used as a powerful adjunct to other systems of healing.

Details of Astrologers can be obtained from:

The Secretary
British Astrological and Psychic Society
124 Trefoil Crescent
Broadfield, Crawley RH11 9EZ

Sue Griffin: Consultant Astrologer for BAPS
2 Kerswell Cottages, Exminster
Exeter, Devon EX6 8AY

LONDON

The Faculty Astrological Studies   071-7003556

SUSSEX

Visionary Designs, P.O. Box 1177, Brighton BN1 1RX.
Tel: 0566 85243 Fax: 0566 85540

AURICULOTHERAPY

Auriculotherapy, or, to be precise, auricular acupuncture, is a specialised form of acupuncture using points in the outer ear.

The potency of the ear points was recognised by the early Chinese acupuncturists and has since been developed, mainly in China and Europe, by modern practitioners.

Demand for treatment is increasing, largely as a result of its simplicity, safety and effectiveness.

Acupuncture points can be located and treated in a number of ways ranging from traditional needles to modern electronic methods. A wide range of conditions often respond quickly to treatment – e.g. allergies, muscular, nervous, digestive, respiratory, addictions etc.

There is a register of trained practitioners held by "The Association of Auriculotherapy G.B. Ltd." which itself is a member of the B.C.M.A. for alternative and complementary medicine.

Enquiries regarding the association, training, and practitioners, can be obtained from the Secretary:

Mr John Lewis
11 Level Lane, Buxton
Derbyshire SK17 6TU

AUTOGENIC TRAINING THERAPY

AUTOGENIC TRAINING is a system of PROFOUND RELAXATION AND STRESS RELEASE which allows the mind to calm itself by switching off the body's stress response.

Following an individual assessment, the training is taught to small groups or individuals, over an 8–10 week period, with practice at home three times daily, and keeping a diary to assess progress. The method involves mental repetition of AUTOGENIC FORMULAE relating to the body in its relaxed state, while remaining the PASSIVE OBSERVER of the process.

The resulting AUTOGENIC STATE allows the brain's self-regulating processes to work naturally, balancing right and left brain activities. This powerfully enhances SELF-HEALING by boosting the immune system, and usually brings greater EMOTIONAL BALANCE and the RELEASE OF CREATIVITY.

It was developed over 60 years ago and is now practised in many countries where it has been medically well-researched and applied to numerous conditions like stress disorders, high blood pressure, asthma, digestive disorders, irritable bowel syndrome, headaches, tremors, epilepsy, insomnia, anxiety states, tranquilliser withdrawal, unresolved grief reactions etc. It has a proven record in sports performance, being used by Olympic athletes, and in personal support for those in hazardous or demanding professions.

THE BRITISH ASSOCIATION FOR AUTOGENIC TRAINING AND THERAPY (BAFATT) a registered charity, acts as the training, research and supervisory body for Autogenic Training in the U.K.

Dr Alice Greene, Hon. Sec. BAFATT,
86 Harley Street, London W1N 1AE

BERKSHIRE

Tamara Burnet-Smith, B.A.F.A.T.T., A.H.P.P.
Autogenic Training ● Profound Relaxation ● Promotes healing processes ● release of creativity ● minimal therapist-dependency ● non-drug approach to a wide range of disorders.
71 Westfield Road, Caversham, Reading RG4 8HL
Tel: 0734 479 957

ESSEX/SUFFOLK

Joan Searle, B.A.   0787 281065

HERTFORDSHIRE

Christine Pinch, S.R.N.   0727 51574

LEICESTERSHIRE

Dr M. K. Arora, M.B.B.S., D.A.B., 4 Meadow Close, Wolvey, Hinckley,
Leicestershire   0455 220464 after 7pm

LONDON

Velta Wilson, M.C.S.P., Crouch End, London N8   081 340 5279

Valerie Bonnefin, BAC accredited counsellor, 83 Nottingham Terrace,
London NW1 4QE   071 486 6367

Dr Alice Greene, M.R.C.G.P., M.F.Hom., Teaches group and individual
at 86 Harley Street, W1N 1AE   071 580 4188

Dr. BRIAN KAPLAN, M.B.B.CH, M.F.Hom
Autogenic Training (BAFATT)
136 Harley Street, London W1N 1AH
Telephone: 071-487 3416

BACH FLOWER REMEDIES

The Bach Flower Remedies are a natural, safe form of healing. They are given to restore peace of mind to the sufferer and help relieve negative attitudes which may be standing in the way of health and happiness.

They were discovered by an eminent physician, Dr. Edward Bach M.B., B.S., L.R.C.P., D.P.H. who dedicated his life to the healing of the sick and was determined in the quest to discover a harmless and simple means of bringing that about. The 38 remedies, each for a different mood, emotion or personality type, together with Rescue Remedy, the composite for emergencies, gently restore the balance between mind and body by helping the sufferer overcome worry, hopelessness, irritability and so on, which hinder recovery and through which the true cause of their discomfort may lie.

The Bach Flower Remedies, established in 1936, are now extensively used throughout the world, forming an integral part of the whole healing spectrum, and because they are so benign and gentle in their action, are an excellent supportive therapy.

Dr Bach lived and worked at Mount Vernon and that cottage has remained the nucleus of his work ever since.

Further information about the Remedies and training for practitioners can be obtained from:

The Bach Centre, Mount Vernon
Sotwell, Wallingford
Oxon. OX10 0PZ
(S.A.E. would be appreciated)

BACH FLOWER REMEDIES

HERTFORDSHIRE

Margaret Izod, M.D.M.A., Bach Flower, Acupuncture, Homoeopathy, Reflexology, 44a High Street, Hoddesdon, Herts EN11 8DA
0992 443462 or 0279 651063

LONDON

The Nutri Centre: Specialists in Vitamin & Nutritional Supplements including Practitioners Products, 7 Park Crescent, London W1N 3HE   071-436 5122 FAX 071-436 5171

Barbara Stanhope-Williamson, M.A.R.
(Registered Counsellor with the Bach Foundation)
Flat 5, 60 West End Lane, West Hampstead NW6
Telephone 071 625 6925

Joan Szinay, B.A., L.C.H., M.H.M.A.(U.K.)   081-449 3626
Violet Hill Studios   071-624 6101

NEWCASTLE UPON TYNE

Natural Health Centre, Talbot House, 17 The Bigg Market, Newcastle upon Tyne NE1 1UN   091-261 9483

SOMERSET

Complementary Medicine Centre, 9 Corporation Street, Taunton, Somerset TA1 4AJ   0823 325022

June Markham, S.P.Dip.A., M.I.S.P.A., The S.E.E.D. Institute, 93A Ilchester Road, Yeovil, Somerset BA21 3BJ   0935 74379
See our Ad under Courses & Tuitions

SURREY

Farnham Holistic Centre, Tilford Road, Farnham, Surrey GU9 8HU   0252 734445

SUSSEX

The Floatarium, 21 Bond Street, Brighton BN1 1RD
0273 679555 Fax: 0273 601992

THE BATES METHOD

Poor sight often reflects disturbance of mental, emotional or physical health, or habits of strain which upset the normal co-ordination of mind and body.

Teachers of the Bates Method use a broadly holistic approach which seeks to identify the causes of poor vision in the individual case and the most appropriate form of treatment, together with exercises in relaxation, memory, imagination and perception, which are used to improve the feedback between eyes and brain, allowing the eyes to function more normally.

The method has been found helpful in all the conditions for which glasses are normally prescribed and has a long history of success with 'difficult' conditions such as squints and 'lazy eyes', even where these are of long standing. In combination with suitable therapies, it can also play a valuable supporting role in the healing of eye disease. it is especially valuable as a *preventive* approach: one should always seek advice at the first indication of trouble.

A list of teachers, details of short courses and teacher training information will be sent on request (please enclose sae 9"×6").

The Bates Association of Great Britain
Friars Court, 11 Tarmount Lane
Shoreham by Sea,
West Sussex BN43 6RQ

HERTFORDSHIRE

Margaret E. Montgomery
Teacher of The Bates Method of Eye Improvement
Hertfordshire & London W1
For All Appointments Ring: 0442 862228

LONDON

Anthony Attenborough
Teacher of the BATES METHOD and
BATES KINESIOLOGY
for improving sight naturally without glasses
128 Merton Road, London SW18 5SP
Tel: 081-874 7337

David Glassman, 26 Cleveland Gardens NW2 1DY   081 455 1317

WEST SUSSEX

Peter Mansfield,   0273 452623

BIOENERGETIC MEDICINE

Bioenergetic medicine covers systems of medical diagnosis and therapy based upon the measurement of electrical energy flows in the body. By stimulating various acupuncture points with minute electrical currents, it is possible to measure the energetic efficiency of various organs and tissues. The electrical energy from the afflicted part is filtered and strengthened in order to bring about an optimum performance of that organ. By utilising the energy of the various organs, a very pure form of therapy results whereby the body is encouraged to heal itself.

Dr A. J. Scott-Morley
Institute of Bioenergetic Medicine
103 North Road, Parkstone, Poole, Dorset
Tel: 0202 733762

BIOFEEDBACK

Biofeedback machines can indicate our response to emotional or challenging situations. Some measure how we cope with stress. We say "something is a pain in the neck" because we are tensing muscles as though we were dealing with danger. The Electromyograph (EMG) machine can read this muscle tension. There are many other phrases (e.g. "I can't stomach that". "I have cold feet about" . . .) which link with responses to danger and point to a biofeedback method which can teach us something about ourselves.

Measurement of the electrical rhythms of the brain, e.g. alpha, can show us different facets of relaxation. Some people can relax their body but not their mind, others need to do some physical activity such as Yoga before they can experience the taste of true relaxation. Working with the beta rhythm of activity, the alpha rhythm of letting be, the theta rhythm of the unconscious allows us to carry calmness into our daily life so that we become more creative and more able to present ourselves well in difficult social situations.

G. G. Blundell
Audio Limited, 26–28 Wendell Road
London W12 9RT
Tel: 081-743 1518

BIOMAGNETIC THERAPY

Biomagnetic therapy combines the art of Traditional Acupuncture and Osteopathy with the ancient healing power of Magnets, without patient apprehension or the hazards of needles.

It provides a safe painless balancing power to the body's own energy field. Biomagnetic Therapy can be used to directly affect the muscular system, freeing joints without the strain of Osteopathic manipulation or massage. The balance produced, releases energy which is induced into the body's own repair system so promoting improved general health.

Using the natural healing power of the body, Biomagnetic treatment is ideal for Organic or Structural conditions, both Acute and Chronic, but especially so, in stress related problems.

For a qualified practitioner in your area please contact:

The British Biomagnetic Association
31 St Marychurch Road
Torquay, Devon TQ1 3JF
Tel: 0803 293346

BODY ELECTRONICS

Body Electronics uses nutrient saturation followed by a revolutionary method of sustained point holding. Pressure on the points causes crystals in the DNA to dissolve and release their stored memory. Dissolving of these crystals is accompanied by the burning of the 'kundalini', which the patient will feel in the area being healed. This method not only releases traumas from one's own life, but also genetic memories, passed on from parents, grandparents etc. This allows hereditary illnesses to be healed. We see all illness as resulting from negative thought patterns stored at the genetic level. Releasing these negative patterns allows the body to function with much greater efficiency, so that it is able to heal and repair itself. Body Electronics has been successful in healing many physical defects, including cancers, arthritis and paralysis, as well as releasing many emotional and mental blocks, and raising consciousness.

Peter Azis
P.O. Box 933
Glastonbury, Somerset

CHEIROLOGY

Cheirology is the study of the features of the hands with an emphasis on the psychological analysis of an individual and on the diagnosis of health, illness and disease. Modern techniques of analysis draw on both oriental Buddhist traditions and Western scientific investigations to create an assessment of the individual at every level of being and these have proven to be of especial value in the analysis of psychological and emotional patterns and in the early diagnosis of arising disease conditions. This has established both the psychological and medical importance of the hand as a diagnostic tool. The hand reveals significant clues to our genetic patterns and dispositions, the current state of our health, our psychological and emotional patterns and experiences, our vocational preferences and inclinations and also our spiritual aspirations. It is thus a powerful tool for gaining insight and self-understanding into who and what we are as individuals, a tool for growth and development and the empowerment of ourselves that we might become more whole.

If you are interested in learning more about cheirology please write for details of classes and seminars, correspondence tuition, practitioners and consultants and society membership (enclosing SAE) to:

Christopher Jones
Cheirological Society Secretary
16 Bridge Street
Osney, Oxford OX2 0BA

LONDON/OXFORD

Christopher Jones, B.A., I.D.C.S., Tuition & Consultations in both London and Oxford   **0865 241086**

NORFOLK

Johnny Fincham, B.A., I.D.C.S., Professional Consultations & Tuition, 39 Union Street, Norwich NR2 2SL   **0603 666646**

CHELATION THERAPY

Chelation therapy with EDTA, a synthetic amino acid, is a long established method for treating acute lead and other heavy metal poisoning. Its use has been successfully extended to treat all forms of heart disease, angina and peripheral blood vessel disease and their consequences. A significant body of scientific literature has been built up over the past ten years showing its effectiveness in treating these conditions. Its role as an important preventive health measure, especially in connection with chronic low-level heavy metal exposure (lead, cadmium, aluminium, mercury), the most prevalent pollution burden, is worthy of consideration. Several long-term studies indicate that it may have an important place in the prevention of cancers. It can safely and usefully be combined with Ozone therapy and other nutritional or other orthodox and complementary therapies.

Dr F. Schellander
Liongate Clinic, 8 Chilston Road
Tunbridge Wells, Kent TN4 9LT
Tel: 0892 543535

CHILDBIRTH

WATER BIRTH

Water birth seems to be something that everybody has heard of but relatively few people know anything about. One thing is certain though, it is becoming increasingly popular in the UK. Probably the main reason for this is that the effect of relaxing in a warm pool of water is a good substitute for medical pain relief.

During pregnancy, women are advised not to take drugs which can affect their unborn child, so it would seem wise to try to avoid them during labour, if possible, as we now know they can cross the placenta and reach the fetus. With the increasing awareness of certain short-term and probably long-term side effects of using drugs, such as pethidine or epidural, many women are now looking for safer alternatives.

A water birth pool provides a form of pain relief and can ease labour pains for many women. The body's own natural pain killers, known as endorphins, are secreted as the mother-to-be relaxes in warm water. This gives her a feeling of well-being, which is transmitted to her baby.

The pool provides most women with a sense of privacy and security and it is easy for them to move into comfortable positions with the buoyancy of the water giving support. Probaby the best time to enter the water is when labour is fully established, at about 5–6cm dilation of the cervix, when the effect of the warm water usually helps to shorten the remainder of the labour. It is possible for the fetal heartbeat to be monitored under water.

To arrange a water birth on the NHS contact the Director of Midwifery at your local hospital

For more information on water birth, workshops and pool hire contact:

Splashdown Water Birth Services
17 Wellington Terrace
Harrow-on-the-Hill, Middlesex
Tel: 081-422 9308

MASSAGE IN PREGNANCY

Profound changes take place in a woman at this time, both physiological and psychological, affecting every aspect of her being. Massage can therefore be invaluable throughout the pregnancy and beyond.

The muscular system which is being subjected to extra tensions can be kept supple, thus preventing the adverse effects that these stresses can cause to ligaments, tendons and joints. Back pain can be alleviated and even prevented, and cramps that may occur, successfully treated.

The beneficial effects on the vascular, lymphatic, nervous and hormonal systems can improve poor circulation, lift depression and alleviate headaches caused by vascular congestion. Massage will clear toxins from the system, and help prevent the formation of varicose veins.

Most importantly the nurturing effect of a good massage can make the mother feel happy and relaxed and if it is her partner who is massaging her, it can stimulate the bonding process between mother, father and baby.

Above all, it can be invaluable during the actual birth and beyond, helping the body's readjustment. It is of course most important to be aware of all contra-indications and to co-operate with the medical and nursing staff attending the pregnant mother.

Susanne Templer, I.S.T.M.Dip.
The West London School of Therapeutic
** Massage**
41a St Luke's Road, London W11 1DD
Tel: 071-229 4672

National Childbirth Trust (NCT)
9 Queensborough Terrace, London W2 3TB
Tel: 071-267 3006

CHINESE MEDICINE

Chinese Medicine comprises Chinese Herbal Medicine, Clinical Massage Therapy, Acupuncture and Qi Gong. It has a history of continuous development over the last 2500 years. During this time principles of diagnosis and treatment of disease have been refined to a high degree of accuracy by the cumulative experience of centuries of Chinese doctors.

Chinese Medicine works on very different principles from Western Medicine, principles which may seem strange when viewed from the mechanistic standpoint. Yet Chinese Medicine is the world's second largest medical system, serving 1.5 billion people worldwide. Chinese Medicine is fully integrated as a medicine in its own right into the Public Health systems of present-day China and Japan and is recognised by the World Health Organisation.

Robert Cran, M.A., M.R.C.H.M.
Vice-chairperson, Register of Chinese
** Massage Therapy**
Principal, London School of Chinese
** Massage Therapy**
49b Onslow Gardens, London N10 3JY
Tel: 081-444 0103

CHINESE HERBAL MEDICINE

Herbal medicine has always been part of traditional medicine in China. Like acupuncture, its practice dates back over two thousand years.

Chinese herbal medicine, like acupuncture, is used to alter the balance and flow of Qi (vital force) in the body. Individual herbs have specific characteristics so that each affects the body's Qi in different ways.

Herbs are usually combined in formulae, or prescriptions, to treat disease. These presciptions have been tried and tested over the centuries and their effects are well documented in Chinese medical literature. The art of Chinese herbal medicine is being able to vary these formulae and tailor them according to each patient's disharmony.

Herbs are used for a wide range of conditions. They are particularly useful for chronic conditions, which may require treatment over several months.

They also offer effective ways to combat acute infections by eliminating harmful pathogens and, by restoring healthy circulation of Qi and Blood.

Geoff Wadlow, M.R.T.C.M.
London School of Acupuncture
** and Traditional Chinese Medicine**
Third Floor, 36 Featherstone Street
London EC1Y 8QX
Tel: 071-490 0513

ESSEX

Richard Ashrowan, M.C.Hb.P.A., M.Ac.P.A.   0206 330928
OR 0206 561150

CHINESE MEDICINE

ACUPUNCTURE

Acupuncture is a traditional Oriental method of healing, which is around 3,000 years old. The ancient Chinese perceived a fundamental energy called Qi which flows around the body through meridians which are near the exterior of the body, and also course internally joining each other and the internal organs.

If the flow of Qi is neither deficient or excessive nor obstructed by coldness, heat, dampness or dryness, then the person will feel in good health.

Should one of these imbalances occur in the circulation of Qi then disharmonies will occur leading to symptoms.

During your initial consultation the practitioner will ask you about every aspect of your health condition. Your whole medical history will be recorded and the physician will feel the pulses at both wrists and examine your tongue. On this basis a diagnosis will be made and some acupuncture points selected.

Using fine stainless steel needles, these points will be punctured creating a change in the flow of Qi in the meridians.

With the appropriate number of treatments a harmony of energy will be achieved and the symptoms will abate.

Acupuncture is effective in treating a wide range of both chronic and acute conditions.

Lotus Healing Centre
129 Queens Cresent, London NW5
Tel: 071-284 4614

CHINESE CLINICAL MASSAGE THERAPY

Chinese Massage Therapy incorporates a wide variety of often difficult techniques both strong and mild, static and dynamic, including touch of all kinds from pressure to the level of subtle energy; stretching; manipulation; assisted exercise; and many others. It originated in Chinese Medicine some time before Christ.

Tui Na is the Chinese name for Chinese Clinical Massage Therapy as practiced in hospitals in the Peoples' Republic of China. For accurate clinical management of illness Tui Na according to TCM differentiation represents the optimum massage treatment. In principle both Tui Na and An Mo are part of the same tradition, namely Chinese Massage Therapy.

Chinese Clinical Massage Therapy is based on the understanding of ill health in terms of the flow of the body's energies. When the flow is perverted or the vitality depleted then illness occurs. Chinese Clinical Massage Therapy aims to integrate the body's energies and fluids harmoniously in order to treat illness accurately and establish good health. It does this by regulating channels of flow in the body and by activating methodically selected groups of points and zones with specific ranges of influences on the body's functions.

Register of Chinese Massage Therapy
12 Norfolk Road, Cliftonville
Margate, Kent CT9 2HY

The Chinese Medicine Clinic, Muswell Hill, N10, Chinese Herbal Medicine, Chinese Clinical Massage Therapy, Acupuncture **081-444 0103**

CHINESE MEDICINE

CHI-KUNG (QI GONG)

True good health is both external and internal. In order to be truly healthy, you must have a healthy physical body and calm and healthy mind. According to Chinese medicine, many illnesses are caused by imbalances in your mind. For example, worry and nerves can upset your stomach; fear or fright can affect the normal function of your kidneys and bladder.

Chi-Kung is a gentle but powerful exercise for health allowing the individual to find balance in body and mind. Through the exercise we co-ordinate mind, body and breath to mobilise and direct chi to heal ourselves and to help in the healing of others.

John Brewer
Community Health Foundation
188 Old Street, London EC1V 9BP
Tel: 071-251 4076 or 081-536 1894

CHIROPRACTIC

Chiropractors specialise in diagnosing and treating disorders of the spine, joints and muscles.

The term chiropractic means treatment by hand or manipulation. It is the third largest healing profession after medicine and dentistry and worldwide there are 50,000 qualified chiropractors.

On a patient's first visit, the qualified chiropractor will take a thorough case history and carry out a full neurological and orthopaedic examination. X-rays may also be taken to check for any abnormalities or conditions which will show if another form of treatment would be more appropriate.

Once these examinations are complete, the chiropractor carries out a detailed analysis of how the individual bones, joints and muscles move, to identify the specific problem area.

Treatment consists of gently unlocking the stiff joints with skilled manipulation by hand, known as adjustment. Quick, comfortable adjustments are used with just the right amount of pressure to restore proper function and mobility to joints.

People usually seek chiropractic treatment for pain caused by accident, injuries at work, poor posture or sports injuries, but it is not only back pain and leg pain that can be eased with chiropractic care; neck pain, arm pain and headaches can also respond well to treatment.

Research carried out by the British Medical Research Council and published by the British Medical Journal in 1990, showed that patients who had received chiropractic treatment had improved by 70 per cent more than those given hospital out-patient care.

The British Chiropractic Association (BCA) is the representative body for the profession and maintains a register of fully qualified chiropractors.

It is important to ensure that your chiropractor is properly qualified. All members undergo six years of full time training and obtain an M.Sc. degree and abide by the code of ethics and rules set down by the Association. Appointments can be made with your local Chiropractor by calling:

Freephone 0800-212 618
British Chiropractic Association
Premier House, 10 Greycoat Place
London SW1P 1SB

McTIMONEY-CORLEY CHIROPRACTIC

McTimoney-Corley Chiropractic is taught at the Witney School of Chiropractic Ltd., which is affiliated to the Further Education Department of Peers School, Oxford. Students receive a four year training based on a modular Open Learning System in the Philosophy, Art and Science of Chiropractic as originated by D. D. Palmer in America and developed by John McTimoney, D.C. and Hugh Corley, D.C. (O.S.C.).

McTimoney-Corley Chiropractors are trained to assess the patient's problems based on current symptoms and past medical history, to use a highly refined, gentle and effective 'whole body' manipulative treatment and to advise on prophylactic exercises based on an awareness of the patient's daily habits.

The British Association for Applied Chiropractic (B.A.A.C.) is the professional regulatory body McTimoney-Corley Chiropractors, governing the Code of Ethics, providing discipline, maintaining professional standards and a register of qualified practitioners.

CHIROPRACTIC

The B.A.A.C. is a member of the Chiropractic Registration Steering Group and the King's Fund working Party on Chiropractic formed to report on the need and basis for legislation for the regulation of Chiropractic, and to provide common codes of Conduct, Ethics and Standards for all registered Chiropractors.

The British Association for Applied Chiropractic P.O. Box 69, Witney, Oxford OX8 5YD

INSTITUTE OF PURE CHIROPRACTIC
14 Park End Street, OXFORD OX1 1HH
Telephone: 0865 246687

McTimoney Chiropractic is a particularly gentle and effective whole body manipulative technique. It aims to correct the alignment of the bones of the spine and other joints of the body, to restore nerve function, to alleviate pain and to promote natural health. Wherever possible, McTimoney chiropractors work in co-operation with the patient's own doctor.

You can be sure of a safe, relatively gentle and professional treatment from a qualified McTimoney Chiropractor. For a directory of practitioners in your area who are licenced and registered with the Institute of Pure Chiropractic please write to the above address enclosing a large self addressed envelope for the attention of The Administrator. For telephone enquiries please call this number:

0993 881861

DERBYSHIRE

Natural Choice Therapy Centre, 24 St John Street, Ashbourne, Derbyshire DE6 1GH   0335 46096

LONDON

Kay McCarroll, D.H.P., M.C., M.I.P.C.
McTimoney Chiropractor/Sports Muscle Therapist.
The Hendon Practice, 12 Golders Rise, London, NW4.
Tel: 081-202 9747

Rebecca Cowley, Chiropractor, C.P., A.I.P.C., The South London Natural Health Centre   071-720 8817

Ray Swaine, Chiropractor, C.P., A.I.P.C., The South London Natural Health Centre   071-720 8817

ALL HALLOWS HOUSE
Centre for Natural Health and Counselling,
Idol Lane EC3 (by Monument tube)
McTimoney Chiropractors
Jane McWhirter, M.A., M.C., M.I.P.C. and
Sue Cartlidge, B.A., M.C., M.I.P.C.
Open Monday–Friday 9am–7pm
for Effective, Gentle, Holistic Back Care
Tel: 071 283 8908

LOTHIAN

Shian Corley, M.A., L.C., M.B.A.A.C.
Registered McTIMONEY–CORLEY Chiropractor
for gentle and effective treatment.
211 Morningside Road, Edinburgh EH10 4QT
Telephone: 031-447 7628

OXFORD

Jillian Baldwin, M.A., L.C., (W.S.C.)   0608 810 429

SOMERSET

Complementary Medicine Centre, 9 Corporation Street, Taunton, Somerset TA1 4AJ   0823 325022
or Redgate Medical Centre, Westonsoyland, Bridgwater, Somerset TA6 5BF   0278 444411

McTIMONEY/CORLEY TYPE OF CHIROPRACTIC

The gentle way of manipulation (for Human and Animal)

Dr. GERDJAN J.B.WEEVERS STOUS,
M.B., B.S., D.C., A.C., F.B.A.A.C

LITTLE HAYES
MILLMOOT LANE
COSSINGTON   TEL: CHILTON POLDEN
SOMERSET TA7 8LW   (0278) 723131

TYNE & WEAR

B.A.A.C.
THE BRITISH ASSOCIATION FOR APPLIED CHIROPRACTIC
REGISTERED OFFICE: P.O. Box 69 Witney Oxon OX8 5YD

Nazir A Kasar
Doctor of Chiropractic (W.S.C.), F.B.A.A.C.
HON.M.D.(M.A.)
McTimoney–Corley Type
SYMPATHETIC PERSONAL CONSULTATION AND ADVICE.
WE TREAT THE CAUSE RATHER THAN THE SYMPTOM
TEL: (091) 273 2040 – FAX: (091) 226 0977
42 BRIGHTON GROVE, FENHAM,
NEWCASTLE UPON TYNE NE4 5NS

YORKSHIRE

Sarah K. Barton, D.C. and partners, Doncaster Chiropractic Clinic (Members of the B.C.A.). For information and leaflet phone   0302 311322

COLONIC HYDROTHERAPY

Forms of Colonic Hydrotherapy have been used from about 1500 B.C., and since used in traditional, orthodox and naturopathic medicine. The basic technique remains the same, but hygiene and standards of practice have progressed making this therapy safe and effective.

Rapid improvements may be realised in motility disorders of the bowel, such as constipation, spastic colon, and some cases of Irritable Bowel Syndrome, as well as abdominal bloating.

Poor elimination can itself lead or contribute to many chronic conditions apparently unrelated to the bowel: halitosis, headaches, skin problems, asthma, allergies, fatigue and some complex conditions such as Candida, M.E. and Crohn's Disease. Colonic Hydrotherapy is of benefit to such conditions when used as part of an integrated approach.

Conducted by a trained therapist, filtered water at a carefully regulated temperature is introduced into the rectum and guided progressively around the whole structure of the colon; using special massage techniques, faecal matter and impacted deposits are expelled and piped away with the water. The process takes about 40 minutes and is safer than using purgatives, laxatives or enemas, since no irritation occurs and no dependency results. Colonic International Association members abide by a strict Code of Conduct, ensuring patient confidence in treatment.

Hon. Secretary Jean Clarke
Colonic International Association
50A Morrish Road, Streatham
London SW2 4EG

DEVON

Roger Groos, B.Sc., D.H.M., R.C.T., M.C.I.A.,
Peggies, Beach Road, Woolacombe, Devon, EX34 7AE   0271 870436

KENT

The Sandown Clinic for Complementary Medicine
171 Sandown Road, Deal, Kent CT14 6NX
Tel: 0304 364879
Contact: **S. C. Fairley**, C.I.A.

LONDON

Wholeness, 26 Mulberry Way, South Woodford, London E18 1ED   081-530 8804

WEST MIDLANDS

COLOUR THERAPY

Light is an energy which becomes visible because of the original energy of darkness. Both are needed by all living structures on this planet. Colours are differentiated light. As the vibrations slow down through the spectrum, we can use all colours of light to change the wellbeing or otherwise of plants, animals and humans. The professional colour practitioner can use all colours to improve health. Even in the ancient Egyptian culture this was known and used. The training is now available again and is a serious study which ends up with examinations, is certificated and the practitioner or healer has to obey a code of ethics and practice. Insurance is needed as is to be an accepted member of the British Register of Complementary Practitioners (B.R.C.P.). This is to protect the public from being treated by individuals who have little or no training.

The use of the powers of colour can change blood pressure, help respiratory problems, migraine, stress, and digestive disorders. Consultations are no less than one hour and the teaching of the patient is an in-built practice so that he or she can learn to improve together with the practitioner.

Red contracts and is Energy. Orange cheers up depression and causes joy. Yellow detaches and enables objectivity. Green balances and cleanses;

turquoise strengthens the immune system. Blue relaxes and helps against high blood pressure. Violet causes self-respect and dignity and magenta helps to let go of old, unnecessary thoughts, feelings and activities.

Theo Gimbel
Hygeia Studios, Colour-Light-Art Research
Incorporating The Hygeia College of Colour
Therapy Ltd.
Brook House, Avening
Tetbury GL8 8NS
Tel: 045 383 2150

Association of Colour Therapists
c/o/ ICM, 21 Portland Place
London W1 3AS

The Hygeia College of Colour Therapy

member of the British Register of Complementary Practitioners.

Complete Professional Colour Therapy Training

Details: *Brook House, Avening, Tetbury, Glos. GL8 8NS*
Telephone: 0453 832150 or 081-204 7672

LONDON

Aura Soma colour healing, body/auric massage, Heather Morgan   071-237 9351

Violet Hill Studios   071-624 6101/081-458 5368

Pauline Wills M.I.A.C.T., H.D.C.Th., M.B.R.A.
Courses on Colour Therapy
and on The Use of Colour with
Reflexology.
Treatment by Appointment
Details: 081-204 7672

SURREY

The Pearl Healing Centre, Colour and Crystal Courses
                                                    081-689 1771

SUSSEX

Visionary Designs, PO Box 1177, Brighton BN1 1RX   0566 85243
                                            FAX: 0566 85540

COUNSELLING

The overall aim of counselling is to provide an opportunity for the client to work towards living in a more satisfying and resourceful way. The term 'counselling' includes work with individuals, pairs or groups of people, often, but not always, referred to as 'clients'. The objectives of particular counselling relationships will vary according to the client's needs. Counselling may be concerned with developing mental issues, addressing and resolving specific problems, making decisions, coping with crisis, developing personal insight and knowledge, working through feelings of inner conflict or improving relationships with others. The counsellor's role is to facilitate the client's work in ways which respect the client's values, personal resources and capacity for self-determination. The counselling relationship must be entered voluntarily.

British Association for Counselling
1 Regent Place, Rugby
Warwickshire CV21 2PJ
Office: 0788 550899
Information: 0788 578328

NARCONON DRUG & ALCOHOL REHABILITATION PROGRAMME

- A truly workable road out for drug and alcohol abusers.
- Comfortable drug-free withdrawal.
- Uses sauna, nutritional supplements and exercise.
- Has a 75% success rate of keeping people off drugs for good
- Gets the person back in control his/her life.
- Methods developed by L. Ron Hubbard

CALL 0892 661562
31a High Street, East Grinstead, Sussex

Offer a safe, supportive
environment for people wishing to:
★ Make positive life changes
★ Feel confident and be in control
★ Communicate effectively and assertively
★ Gain further self-awareness, expression and creativity
Through:
★ One to one counselling and Gestalt therapy
★ Groupwork   ★ Workshops
Professional Supervision and Training also offered
★ INITIAL CONSULTATION FREE
★ Concessions available
Led by experienced Counsellor/Trainers
Christine Wood and **Jimmy McGhee**
For Further Information Contact
Resource Workshops on 081-840 4385

RESOURCE WORKSHOPS

COUNSELLING

COUNSELLING

LOTHIAN

Sarah Cantelo   031-551 5091

Ishtar Swaffield, Cert.Ed., Cert.Psych., Cert.Couns., Psychotherapy   031-551 5091

Nirved Wilson, B.Sc., Dip.S.W., Eriksonian Hypnosis   031- 551 5091

NEWCASTLE UPON TYNE

Natural Health Centre, Talbot House, 17 The Bigg Market, Newcastle upon Tyne NE1 1UN   091-261 9483

SUFFOLK

Confused? Whatever the problem, **A Life Direction Consultation** will help you move forward. Tel: Peter Clifford on 0787 371798

SURREY

Farnham Holistic Centre, Tilford Road, Farnham, Surrey GU9 8HU   0252 734445

CRANIO-SACRAL THERAPY

Cranio-Sacral Therapy is a comprehensive therapy which treats the whole person by very gently balancing the membranes, bones, fluids and fascia throughout the body, which together make up the Cranio-Sacral System, thereby bringing the person into balance on all levels.

Treatment is exceptionally gentle. The practitioner simply places his or her hands very gently on the patient's head, sacrum or other appropriate parts of the body and by application of the softest pressures, balances the subtle twists, pulls and asymmetries reflected through the system.

Cranio-Sacral Therapy works on a very profound level, influencing the central nervous system, and its effects then radiate out to restore healthy function to all parts of the body. It is therefore very effective in identifying and treating the root cause of any problem and in treating the complex chronic effects of injuries and disease.

Cranio-Sacral Therapy treats the whole person; it can therefore help almost any condition – from physical injuries and functional disorders (digestive, menstrual, nervous, etc.) to emotional disturbances and persistent symptoms of obscure origin. Although by no means restricted to conditions affecting the head, it has a very special role to play in the treatment of Birth Trauma and other head injuries and also in treating the after effects of Meningitis and other conditions affecting the meninges.

Complete courses in this gentle yet powerful therapy provide an extensive training in Cranio-Sacral Therapy leading to certification and membership of the Register of Cranio-Sacral Therapists.

Thomas Attlee, D.O., M.R.O., M.R.C.S.T.
Symphysis for the Study of Holistic Health (S.S.H.H.)
160 Upper Fant Road,
Maidstone, Kent ME16 8DJ
Tel: 0622 729231

Cranial Osteopathic Association
478 Baker Street, Enfield, Middlesex EN1 3QS
Tel: 081-367 5561

LONDON

Peter Watt   081-986 6486
Violet Hill Studios   071-624 6101

Thomas Attlee, D.O., M.R.O., M.R.C.S.T.
Primrose Healing Centre, 9 St. George's Mews,
Primrose Hill, London NW1 8XE
Tel: 071 586 0148

Refia Sacks, The Highbury Centre, 137 Grosvenor Avenue, London N5 2NH   071-226 5805 – 071-226 1815

CRANIO-SACRAL THERAPY

LOTHIAN

John Page, D.O., M.G.O., M.Cr.O.A., Cranial Osteopathy
031-551 5091

MIDDLESEX

Release Past Trauma. Realise Your Potential, Babies, Children
081-866 1148

CRYSTAL HEALING/GEM THERAPY

"The way crystals and gemstones are formed in the earth makes them the most stable, organised matter in the universe. Their component atoms are arranged in the most orderly way possible and crystals will make internal adjustments to maintain this orderliness.

It is these qualities that create positive effects on the human energy system. They act like tuning forks to remind us of our potential for balance and health. Each type of stone has a specific energy, a natural resonance, that helps the body correct imbalances at very deep and fine levels.

Careful placement of stones for a few minutes on or around the body, holding or meditating with crystals, gently moving gemstones through the aura and subtle bodies, all significantly help to remove stress and improve the quality of life on physical, emotional, mental and spiritual levels. A relaxing and enjoyable way to promote well-being and get more from living.

Simon Lilly and Sue Griffin, tutors for
The Institute of Crystal and Gem Therapists
2 Kerswell Cottages,
Exminster, Exeter EX6 8AY
Tel: 0392 832005

DEVON

ESSEX

GLOUCESTERSHIRE

LONDON

CRYSTAL HEALING/GEM THERAPY

LOTHIAN

Brigid Gallagher, M.Crys.H., T.D.H.A., I.T.E.C., Acupressure, Reflexology and Electro-crystal Therapy   031-551 5091

GREATER MANCHESTER

Austrian **Prism** Crystal Pendants, wide range of gemstones, send 28p stamp for mail order catalogue to Spirit Guide, 199 Dialstone Lane, Stockport SK2 7LF. Tel/Fax   061-483 3846

SOMERSET

CRYSTAL IMPORTS
IMPORTERS, WHOLESALERS & RETAILERS
Natural Crystals: Top Quality Amethyst, Rock Crystal, Citrine, Quartz, Tourmaline, Calcites, Aquamarine, Ruby, Emerald and many other World wide Mineral Specimens
'NEW AGE' CRYSTALS and SILVER JEWELLERY
Pyramids, Obelisks, Balls and Eggs in Natural and 'Austrian' Crystal, Gem Trees, Crystal Growing Kits, Gemstone Watches and Pens.
*BESIDES A GOOD SELECTION OF 'GIFT ITEMS ·
SOME MADE IN DULCOTE STONE*
'Shop' Times: 9.30 am to 4.30 pm., Monday to Friday
Other Times by Appointment
**DEPT. MS
DULCOTE QUARRY, WELLS,
SOMERSET BA5 3PY ENGLAND
TELEPHONE and FAX: 0749 75827**

STAFFORDSHIRE

CRYSTALS
THOUSANDS OF CRYSTALS — TONS OF ROUGH ROCK
LARGEST STOCKIST of natural stones in the MIDLANDS

All types of Quartz - AMETHYST, CITRINE, AQUA AURA, ROSE, RUTILATED AND SMOKEY
NEW GREEN TOURMALINATED QUARTZ
Other stones - AMBER, TOPAZ, TOURMALINE, SUGALITE, HEMATITE, FLUORITES, MOONSTONE, ZIRCON (Hyacinth), AGATES, etc.

Wholesale/Retail (Lapidary Shop):
Suppliers to Healing Centres,
Gift Shops, Mines & Museums.
CRYSTAL HOLDINGS (Wholesale),
1st Floor,26 WATERLOO ROAD,
BURSLEM, STOKE-ON-TRENT
ST6 3ES. TEL: 0782-810914

POUNDS OF POLISHED STONES — WHOLESALE VAN TRAVELS TO MOST PARTS OF COUNTRY

SURREY

The Pearl Healing Centre, Crystal & Colour Courses   081-689 1771

Farnham Holistic Centre, Tilford Road, Farnham, Surrey GU9 8HU   0252 734445

SUSSEX

The Floatarium, 21 Bond Street, Brighton BN1 1RD   0273 679555
Fax 0273 601 992

Visionary Designs, PO Box 1177, Brighton BN1 1RX   0566 85243
Fax 0566 85540

CYMATICS

The Cymatic therapeutic treatment is applied by a frequency controlled instrument which uses totally controlled acoustic audible sound frequencies and will induce beneficial stimulation, activation and circulation when applied to organic bodies.

The use of controlled sound application to the human body has steadily increased from the first application of medical sonar to the recent magnetic resonance scanning, and have pointed out that sonic stimulus of the human body has produced valid results.

Cymatic therapy, which also includes magnetic radiation as part of its concept, is a totally controlled acoustic and non-acoustic audible sound frequency with a transcutaneous method of transmission penetrating the entire human body.

It requires no medication, medical or surgical procedure, nor does it require chemical administration in any manner. Cymatic therapy is not only a curative entity solely within itself but a system which is capable of stimulating natural regulatory and immunological systems and acts to produce a near optimum metabolic state for that particular part or organ of the human body, bringing about natural changes to enhance its well-being and to overcome any adverse conditions existing in the organ or structure.

**Peter Guy Manners, M.D., D.O., F.I.C.T.M.,
P.L.D., L.B.C.P., D.D., M.H.M.A.
Bretforton Hall Clinic, Bretforton
Vale of Evesham, Worcestershire WR11 5JH
Tel: 0386 830537**

DANCE AND MOVEMENT THERAPY

HEALING DANCE

Healing Dance is about awakening the healer within through connecting to the intrinsic energy of your self. This is done by using the resources of breath, movement, meditation, visualization, rhythm and the voice.

By going through various movement rituals of centreing, stretching, opening and releasing the body, one becomes more in touch with the depth of one's feelings and sensations. Taking time out for this process is important, as this gift of moving in space and time with full attention to the present moment brings about an absorption and unifying of body, mind and spirit. A new surge of energy arises that is directed and channelled with appropriate images/visualizations of strength, vitality, joy, balance and release. New patterns of movement are discovered, coming from within the being's body memory. Through the power of music, voice and drumming, old, negative patterns can be let go so that the Healing Dance can begin with oneself and interaction through contact with others.

**Written by
Martyn Rudin
Open Spirit Dance
Rackclose Lane, Exeter EX4 3AH
Tel: (0392) 422134**

DIANETICS

Dianetics® provides the individual with a workable technology of handling the reactive mind. No drugs, no hypnotism, no mechanical treatment is used. This is the first organised science of the mind built on natural laws.

In *Dianetics*, L. Ron Hubbard isolated the single source of mental problems, stress, worries, lack of confidence and how it will affect health and I.Q. It is the No 1 bestselling self-help book in the world today, with over 15 million sold, for one reason – it works.

A study of Dianetics readers conducted by an independent research company revealed an astounding 81% agreed that Dianetics techniques help people become more successful. 79% said that applying the techniques had changed their lives.

Growing numbers of health professionals are now using Dianetics techniques. Each week thousands of people apply Dianetics techniques for the first time in Dianetics seminars and discover for themselves how to handle the reactive mind with Dianetics.

Dianetics counselling, seminars, professional training, Do-it-Yourself video and books are all available. Receive a free personality test by post or in person at one of the following Dianetics centres around the U.K.

Hubbard Foundation (U.K.)
St. Hill Manor, East Grinstead
W. Sussex
Tel: 081-577 2877

BIRMINGHAM

Birmingham Dianetics Centre
Information Line   081-577 2877

DEVON

Plymouth Dianetics Centre
Information Line   081-577 2877

DORSET

Bournemouth Dianetics Centre
Information Line   081-577 2877

DUBLIN

Dublin Dianetics Centre
Information Line   081-577 2877

EDINBURGH

Edinburgh Dianetics Centre
Information Line   081-577 2877

LONDON

London Dianetics Centre
Information Line   081-577 2877

MANCHESTER

Manchester Dianetics Centre
Information Line   081-577 2877

EAST SUSSEX

Brighton Dianetics Centre
Information Line   081-577 2877

Hove Dianetics Centre
Information Line   081-577 2877

WEST SUSSEX

Chichester Dianetics Centre
Information Line   081-577 2877

East Grinstead Dianetics Centre
Information Line   081-577 2877

TYNE AND WEAR

Sunderland Dianetics Centre
Information Line   081-577 2877

ELECTRO-CRYSTAL THERAPY

Electro-Crystal Therapy combines diagnostic assessment (Electro Scanning Method) and treatment to balance the human energy field in methods which are non invasive. These scientific techniques comprise crystal sound therapy and crystal optical therapy, both combining natural crystals and gem stones with pulsed high frequency electromagnetic waves, using battery operated equipment. All known health disorders can be helped and our practitioners take a very holistic approach.

Electro-Crystal Therapy was invented by biologist Harry Oldfield, who as a practising Christian, fully integrates his Christian beliefs in all his work. He pioneered Kirlian Photography as a medical research tool in the U.K. and abroad. His book 'The Dark Side of the Brain' published by Element Books Ltd, covers the subjects of Kirlian Photography and Electro-Crystal Therapy.

The School of Electro-Crystal Therapy holds regular training courses to Certificate level and now has a large number of qualified practitioners throughout the the U.K. and overseas. It is affiliated to the Institute of Complementary Medicine which enables qualified practitioners to apply for membership of the British Register of Complementary Practitioners.

For further information contact:
The School of Electro-Crystal Therapy
117 Long Drive, South Ruislip
Middlesex HA4 0HL.

HAMPSHIRE

Tony Crowe, M.Sc.E.T.
0252 616751
See under Kinesiology

THE FELDENKRAIS METHOD

The method takes its name from its originator Dr. Moshe Feldenkrais and has its roots in Western Science and Martial Arts. It is concerned with the re-education of movement and is taught in two formats: group classes called "Awareness through Movement", and individual sessions known as "Functional Integration". The aim is to learn to recognise habitual, restrictive ways of moving or holding yourself and then to discover efficient graceful alternatives.

To obtain a directory of teachers of
The Feldenkrais Method, write to:
The Feldenkrais Guild,
P.O. Box 370, London N10 3XA
Stephen Cotton
(on behalf of The Feldenkrais Guild)

DORSET

Wilfred Van Dorp, B.Sc.(Hons), D.Hom.(Med)
33 Vale Road, Poole, Dorset BH14 9AT.
Tel: 0202 747063 – London Tel: 071-328 7374
Home Visiting Service: London & Dorset

LONDON

Garet Ann Newell,
October Gallery, 24 Old Gloucester Street,
London WC1
Telephone: 081-549 9583

EAST SUSSEX

For information on the four-year training in the Feldenkrais Method, the next training to begin in 1995, please write:
Garet Newell
Feldenkrais Professional Training Programme
P.O. Box 1207, Hove, East Sussex BN3 2GG
Tel: 081-549 9583

FENG SHUI

Often translated as the Chinese Art of Placement, Feng Shui aims to create the ultimate living or work space. Chinese experts considered each house or office to have its own subtle flow of energy based on the layout of the property. Using simple objects such as mirrors, lights, plants, wind chimes or crystals this energy can be enhanced or subdued. The flow of this energy will affect the occupants lives in eight ways. Wealth, fame, marriage, family, helping people, career, knowledge and children.

A short course in Feng Shui will provide enough information to actually try it out. The results can be amazing as the Chicago Cubs found out when after a Feng Shui practitioner recommended changes to their stadium they went from last place to become world champions. After a recent Feng Shui seminar a woman realised her office layout reduced her sense of control. Once she made the recommended changes she shortly received the promotion she had been trying for.

Simon Brown
Community Health Foundation
188 Old Street
London EC1V 98P
Tel: 071-251 4076

Michael Keating Feng Shui Consultant   0458 834974

FLOATATION THERAPY

Floatation therapy, or Restricted Environmental Stimulus Therapy, as it is scientifically known, is a technique that enables deep relaxation and stress reduction effortlessly.

It works by temporarily releasing the body from environmental stress and stimulus, and this in turn triggers the body's natural relaxation response. After a shower to eliminate body oils you step into your "Float Tank". This contains a shallow pool of warm water saturated with Epsom salts thus allowing you to "Float" in an atmosphere of complete darkness and tranquility. To ease into this relaxation, soothing music is played for the first few minutes.

It is comforting to know that recent advancements have eliminated causes of claustrophobia and reassures the first time user.

An average float lasting an hour will leave the user feeling refreshed and rejuvenated. The body's stress causing chemicals are reduced and replaced with "endorophins" the body's natural opiate/painkiller. This brings about a profound improvement in physical and mental states for up to two weeks. The natural high and feeling of well being achieved, even after the first session, is incomparable.

Users report feelings of increased creativity, and a decrease of stress related symptoms, thus correcting feelings of "Burn out" and exhaustion.

Toward the end of the hour, soothing music is once again piped through the speakers, so that the user can return refreshed and rejuvenated to the world.

Samantha O'Connor, Director
The Float Centre, 20 Blenheim Terrace
St. John's Wood, London NW8 0EB
Tel: 071-328 7276

Floatation Tank Association (UK)
3A Elms Crescent, London SW4 8QE
Tel: 071-350 1001

Gordon Fricker, M.F.T.A., Floatation Therapist, The South London Natural Health Centre   071-720 8817

FLOWER AND GEM REMEDIES

FLOWER ESSENCES

Flower Essences are liquid potentised plant preparations which convey a distinct imprint of a specific flower. These remedies expand our understanding of health care, recognising a relationship between the emotional, psychological, spiritual, and physical aspects of the person.

Flower essences enjoy a reputation of being not only highly effective, but very safe to use. They are not part of the standard biochemical medicine, for they contain only minute traces of the physical substance. Rather they belong to a pioneering new field of potentised remedies which derive their beneficial powers from the inherent life forces within substances.

Each flower has its own individual signature which corresponds to a different need. For example Bleeding Heart, a flower that looks like the shape of a perfectly formed heart, brings you a feeling of peace coming into your heart releasing you from the pain and grief that is so often associated with affairs of the heart.

The Flower and Gem Remedy Association
Anubis House, Cresswell Drive
Ravenstone, Leicestershire LE6 2AG
Tel: 0530 510864

GEM REMEDIES

Gem Remedies are liquid potentised mineral preparations which convey a distinct imprint of a specific crystal, mineral or semi-precious gemstone. Like the flower essences they work on the emotional, psychological and spiritual as well as physical levels. However they differ from flowers in that they assist more on the physical levels of the body and the emotional aspects of the person. They can help in treating allergies, emotional problems, shock and traumatic situations such as divorce.

The colour of the mineral also plays a part, for example, using Amethyst gem essence, which incorporates the colour purple, has been found to be effective for assisting meditation and releasing tension around the eyes.

The Flower and Gem Remedy Association
Anubis House, Cresswell Drive
Ravenstone, Leicestershire LE6 2AG
Tel: 0530 510864

LONDON

Australian Bush Flower Remedies, New, Powerful vibrational healing. Heather Morgan   071-237 9351

The Nutri Centre: Specialists in Vitamin and Nutritional Supplements including Practitioners Products, 7 Park Crescent, London W1N 3HE   071-436 5122 FAX 071-436 5171

GESTALT THERAPY

Gestalt comes from the German word meaning whole or complete. The wholeness refers to the organism-as-a-whole or mind-body-spirit unity to the integration of all the splits and polarities into a whole person; and also on a fundamental level to the completing or finishing of each situation before moving on.

The process by which we do this involves self awareness: basically collecting information about ourselves – "Who am I?", "What do I want?", "How do I feel?" and how these conflict with the internal demands of "How I should behave?" Bringing these conflicts to the surface enables us to take responsibility for our life so we move from helpless puppets to choiceful and response-able people.

Contact and dialogue between therapist and client is central to the Gestalt method. The therapist uses his/her personality and creativity as well as skills and theory to become an active presence in the relationship. Thus all qualified Gestalt psychotherapists have done years of personal therapy themselves.

John Leary-Joyce
The Gestalt Centre (London) Administration:
64 Warwick Road, St Albans, Herts. AL1 4DL
Tel: 0727 864806

been part of many belief systems for centuries. The ability of a gifted individual to help other members of their tribe seems to be inherent in most race memories.

This ability can be likened to the spark from the plug in an internal combustion engine. It's like a simple transference of energy which starts off an onward going motion, this quickly gathers speed until everything is once again running smoothly.

Healing creates the right environment within others so that their own innate healing power can develop and grow. This in turn can restore the balance of energies, remove any blockages within the system and so allow the body to regain its natural state of well being. All of life has this unique built in potential which is constantly striving towards wholeness.

Depression, stress and anxiety are feelings that can reduce the efficiency of our own body defence systems to attack. Whereas healing can bring about a wonderful sense of well being, promote relaxation and a quiet confidence in one's own ability to think well and to get well!!

Harry Thompson Ph.D.
Professional Holistic Healer
Myrtle Cottage
Ambler Thorn, Queensbury
Bradford BD13 2DJ, West Yorkshire
Tel: 0274 882466

LONDON

SOMERSET

HEALING

Healing by touch is perhaps the most remarkable and yet the most simple of all therapies and has

CHESHIRE

DYFED

ESSEX

HEALING

GLOUCESTERSHIRE

Alice Friend
(formerly Willcocks)

Dove Cottage, 40 Summer Street, Stroud, Glos. GL5 1NT

Tel: 0453 750919

Alice has had experience in medicine wheel work, personal intense therapy, leading workshops, knitting rainbow healing sweaters, writing and bringing up children. She is a trained healer, counsellor and medium. Her work is mainly in mediumship using that as a mirror to reflect answers and unlock the soul's ability to move forward.

Rose Dawson, 20 years experience in Healing–Counselling–Spiritual development, Lecturing and Probationer training. Member of National Fed. of Spiritual Healers. Registered No. B2386
For information Ring:
Cheltenham 0242 228778

Mark Alexander, London/Gloucester. Spiritual Healer, Stress Management, Counselling, Crystal/Past Life Therapist, Balancing Mind, Body, Spirit **0452 385848**

HERTFORDSHIRE

PSYCHIC ONES – SPIRITUAL HEALING SANCTUARY
65 Vicarage Road, Watford, Herts WD1 8EJ
Tel: (0923) 244562 (weekdays)
(0923) 662160 (evenings and weekends)
Leader, Robert Harris-Baird
Member of N.F.S.H., W.F.H., B.A.A.P.S.
Spiritual Healing, Relaxation Tuition, Tarot

Confederation of Healing Organisations at Pheasant Lodge, The Common, Berkhamsted, Herts. HP4 2QF **0442 863089**

HUMBERSIDE

Natural Healing Centre
72 Pasture Road, Goole, North Humberside DN14 6HE. Tel: 0405 769119
Acupuncture ● Bach flowers ● Crystal Healing ● Aromatherapy
Chiropody ● Homoeopathy ● Hypnotherapy ● Iridology ● Remedial
Massage ● Eleven years of Natural therapies in Humberside
We have time to listen.

LONDON

Monica Anthony, M.B.S.H., M.R.C.S.T.
Practitioner in Colour Healing, Hypnotherapy, Cranio-Sacral Therapy, Holistic Foot Massage.
(Courses also available)
Telephone 071-232 2562

Hendon Natural Health Centre
12 Golders Rise, Hendon NW4
McTimoney Chiropractic ● Kinesiology ● Reflexology ● Massage
Small venue available W/E Courses
081-202 9747

Gilly Lewis, N.F.S.H., I.T.E.C. 081-455 2011
Violet Hill Studios 071-624 6101

Marion McGowan, B.A., Career Counselling 081-455 0849
Violet Hill Studios 071-624 6101

Kestrel, Healer, M.C.O.H., N.F.S.H., The South London Natural Health Centre 071-720 8817

NEWCASTLE UPON TYNE

Natural Health Centre, Talbot House, 17 The Bigg Market, Newcastle upon Tyne NE1 1UV **091-261 9483**

SUFFOLK

Re-discover your inner power and optimum health. Experienced healer offers help at reasonable rates. Tel: Peter Clifford on 0787 371798

SURREY

Farnham Holistic Centre, Tilford Road, Farnham, Surrey GU9 8HU **0252 734445**

WORCESTERSHIRE

Lyn Fox, N.F.S.H. Healer, Bewdley, Worcs. **0299 402716**

College of Healing

Patron: Sir George Trevelyan, Bart.
Principals: Ann Neate; Dr. David Smallbone.

The College of Healing offers a 3-part Diploma Course for those who are deeply interested in the art of healing, either as a professional therapy or to enhance their personal development.
For full details contact:
The Secretary, College of healing, Runnings Park, Croft Bank, West Malvern, Worcs. WR14 4DU. Tel: 0684 565253

WEST YORKSHIRE

HELLERWORK

Hellerwork is an integrating process combining structural bodywork, movement education and dialogue; exploring how your body reflects your mind.

The aim is to become free of set patterns; mental and physical, to enhance your ability to adapt more easily to life's changes, and to allow you to use your body in the best possible manner.

Hellerwork is a 'hands-on' treatment releasing chronic tension and rigidity in your body and bringing in balance and alignment. Hellerwork helps you become body aware and gives you new choices in movement, preventing the return of tension. Hellerwork allows you to recognise how your attitudes, thoughts, beliefs and emotions affect your body, further assisting you to discover new ways of dealing with the stress of life.

Joseph Heller (1940–) was an aerospace engineer in Pasadena, California. Later he became the director of Kairos, a Los Angeles centre for human development, and participated in year-long trainings in bioenergetics and gestalt, as well as shorter workshops with Buckminster Fuller, John Lilly, Virginia Satir and Brugh Joy.

Heller became a Rolfer in 1972 and studied with Ida Rolf until 1978, also learning Patterning from Judith Aston. He became the first president of the Rolf Institute in 1975 and left to found Hellerwork in 1978. He now lives in Mt. Shasta, California and practises, and teaches Hellerwork all over the world.

The Institute of Structural Bodywork
c/o Roger Golten, Synergy Centre
1 Cadogen Gardens, London SW3 2RJ

HERBAL PRODUCTS

HELLERWORK

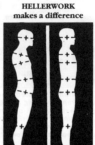
European Professional Training Starts 1994

Contact Practitioners For More Information

HERBAL MEDICINE

Medical Herbalism is the modern Western form of a deep-rooted healing tradition which uses whole plant remedies in the treatment of disease.

It has two aspects. One is the scientific medical approach to consultation in which the procedures followed in physical examination and diagnosis provides a sound basis for evaluation and management of the patient's condition. The other is the individual prescription of herbs in appropriate forms and combinations. The Medical Herbalists's expertise in both areas offers an integrated primary approach to disease treatment, disease prevention and health promotion.

Morag Chacksfield, B.Sc., M.N.I.M.H.
For further information, including a list of
qualified Medical Herbalists,
send a 9½″×6½″ (A5) S.A.E. to:
The National Institute of
Medical Herbalists Ltd.,
9 Palace Gate, Exeter, Devon EX1 1JA

General Council and Register of Consultant Herbalists
Marlborough House, Swanpool
Falmouth, Cornwall TR11 4HW
Tel: 0326 317321

HERBAL MEDICINE

BEDFORDSHIRE

Richard Barnes, M.N.I.M.H., East Beds. Natural Therapy Centre, Sandy **0604 231735**

BUCKINGHAMSHIRE

Mr. J. Briskman, B.A.(Hons.), M.N.I.M.H.
54 Plym Close, Aylesbury, Bucks. HP21 8SX
Tel: 0296 84394

CAMBRIDGESHIRE

Herbal Clinic including Aromatic Medicine, A. Davies, B.Sc., M.N.I.M.H., 19 Swaynes Lane, Comberton **0223 264159**

CASTLE DOUGLAS

HERBALISM
Mrs. P. Tilbury, M.N.I.M.H.
Consultant Medical Herbalist
Sunrise, Old Station Yard, Castle Douglas
Tel: 0556 4455 or 06446 623

DERBYSHIRE

Natural Choice Therapy Centre, 24 St. John Street, Ashbourne, Derbyshire DE6 1GM **0335 46096**

DEVON

Optimum-Phoenix, Swedish Bitters, Herbs, 20% discount **0398 332000**

ESSEX

Mrs S. Koten, M.N.I.M.H.
Registered Medical Herbalist
14 Corbets Avenue, Upminster, Essex RM14 2FQ
Telephone 0708 223524

HAMPSHIRE

HERBALISM and ALLERGY TESTING
Mahmood Chaudhry,
46 Greywell Precinct, Leigh Park,
Havant, Hants. PO9 5AL
Tel: 0705 471781

LONDON

The Nutri Centre: Specialists in Vitamin and Nutritional Supplements including practitioners products. 7 Park Crescent, London W1N 3HE **071-436 5122** FAX **071-436 5171**

Steve Kippax, Herbalist, M.N.R.I.H., M.R.C.H.M., The South London Natural Health Centre **071-720 8817**

LOTHIAN

Zoe Capernaros, M.A., M.N.I.M.H. **031-551 5091**

MERSEYSIDE

H. Simpson, D.O.-N.C.S.O., M.G.O.(Lon.), M.I.C.A.K., M.R.S.H., M.H.P.A., M.A.A., M.C.K.O.R.E. **0744 88 3737**

NORTHAMPTONSHIRE

Richard Barnes, M.N.I.M.H., 25 Burns Street, Northampton **0604 231735**

OXFORDSHIRE

Mrs. N. Manston,
M.N.I.M.H., M.R.O. (Member of Register of Osteopaths)
5 Church Street, Beckley, Oxon OX3 9UT
Tel: 086 735 784

SHROPSHIRE

Nicky Jevon, M.H., Master Herbalist & Naturopath, Herbal Health Care Clinic, 18a Church Street, Oswestry, Shropshire SY11 3SP **0691 658202**

SOMERSET

Complementary medicine Centre, 9 Corporation Street, Taunton, Somerset TA1 4AJ **0823 325022**
or Redgate Medical Centre, Westonsoyland, Bridgwater, Somerset TA6 5BF **0278 444411**

SUFFOLK

Mrs. Marion Gladwell, M.N.I.M.H.
Medical Herbalist
Clinics: Bury St. Edmunds · Hundon · Castle Hedingham
For information and appointments
Telephone 0440 86228

SUSSEX

Registered Medical Herbalist
also Registered Counsellor of Bach Flower Remedies,
Allergy Testing
Whiskers Cottage, Workhouse Lane, Westfield,
Nr. Hastings, East Sussex TN35 4QJ
Telephone (0424) 752376

HOMOEOPATHY

Homoeopathy is a complete system of medicine which assists each patient to deal with the cause of their illness and regain health. It recognises that all symptoms of ill health are signs of disharmony within the whole person, and that each person needs individual treatment.

There are over 2000 different homoeopathic medicines which are prepared in homoeopathic pharmacies to strict specifications. They cannot produce side effects, and are non-addictive.

In order to prescribe accurately for each patient, a homoeopath needs to take a detailed case history. This picture of the patient is matched to the correct homoeopathic remedy. That remedy will then stimulate the patient's own system so that the healing process can begin. Each case is monitored closely by the homoeopath as the treatment progresses.

All homoeopaths registered with the Society of Homoeopaths have undergone an approved training, and practise in accordance with the Society's Code of Ethics.

For more information and register please send a large stamped addressed envelope to:
The Society of Homoeopaths
2 Artizan Road, Northampton NN1 4HU
Tel: 0604 21400

HOMOEOPATHY

Homoeopathy is a medical speciality based on the recognition that like may be treated by like, using the smallest effective dose. The medicines used are employed in treatment on the basis of data compiled clinically by human test, not animal trials.

The suitability of any given medicine used homoeopathically relates to an overview of its effect on the whole human system both in clinical evaluation and medicine use.

Homoeopaths consider it better to treat the sick person rather than the disease, so the patient is treated rather than his/her illness. Because of this approach, patients suffering from the same 'disease' will often require different remedies, while another group of patients with different 'diseases' may benefit from the same remedy.

The treatment is available on the NHS and there are busy Out-patient clinics at hospitals in London, Glasgow, Tunbridge Wells, Liverpool and Bristol. Names and addresses of doctors and veterinary surgeons practising homoeopathy can be obtained from the BHA. Please send S.A.E.

Patron: Queen Elizabeth The Queen Mother
The British Homoeopathic Association
27A Devonshire Street
London W1N 1RJ
Tel: 071-935 2163

HOMOEOPATHY

Ainsworths

HOMOEOPATHIC PHARMACY

* Remedies by return *

38 New Cavendish Street, London W1M 7LH

Prescriptions: 071-935 5330 Fax: 071-486 4313
Answer Phone: 071-487 5253

ORDERS ACCOUNTS BOOKS

40-44 High Street, Caterham, Surrey CR3 5UB
Tel: Caterham (0883) 340332 Fax: (0883) 344602

DERBYSHIRE

Childrens Homoeopathic Clinic (0–5 yrs free), Natural Choice Therapy Centre, Ashbourne, Derbyshire DE6 1GH **0335 46096**

John Coatman, M.A., D.S.H., Natural Choice Therapy Centre, 24 St. John Street, Ashbourne, Derbyshire DE6 1GH **0335 46096**

DEVON

Optimum-Phoenix, Homoeopathic Remedies and Book, 20% Discount offered **0398 332000**

Jeanne Harris, R.S.Hom., D.S.H. **0884 255990**

DORSET

Galen Homoeopathics (J.A. Eiles, M.P.S.)
Postal Service Available
(24 hour Ansaphone Service)
Lewell Mill, West Stafford, Dorchester, Dorset
DT2 8AN. Telephone: Dorchester 0305 263996
Fax 0305 250792

Wilfred Van Dorp, B.Sc.(Hons), D.Hom. (Med),
Natural Health Consultancy,
33 Vale Road, Poole, Dorset BH14 9AT
Tel: Poole 0202 747063
Tel: London 071 328 7374
Home Visits Available

ESSEX

Marion Howie, M.Sc., L.C.M. **0621 828839** or**0206 561150**

Joyce Revett, L.C.H. **0206 305647** or **0206 561150**

Life-Force Centre for natural well-being **0206 250071**

Great Clacton Natural Healing Centre 6 St. John's Road, Great Clacton, Essex **0255 436059**

HAMPSHIRE

Homoeopathy and Allergy Testing
Mahmood Chaudhry,
46 Greywell Precinct, Leigh Park, Havant,
Hants. PO9 5AL. Tel: 0705 471781

HERTFORDSHIRE

Margaret Izod, M.D.M.A., Homoeopathy, Bach Flower, Acupuncture, Reflexology, 44a High Street, Hoddesdon, Herts EN11 8DA **0992 443462** or **0279 651063**

HIGHLANDS

Janet Caine, B.A., L.C.H., P.C.H.
Anthony Walker, B.Sc.
Classical Homoeopaths
Inverness Natural Therapy Centre 0463 711060
Fochabers Natural Therapy Centre 0343 821443
Treatment, Classes and Courses in Highland and Grampian

KENT

Natural Medicine Centre
87 Beckenham Lane, Shortlands, Bromley,
Kent BR2 0DN
Tel: 081-460 1117
Qualified practitioners available daily

LONDON

Dr. M. H. Cox, M.B.B.S.,
386 Upper Richmond Road West,
East Sheen, London SW14 7JU
Telephone: 081-878 3512

Dr. Alice Greene,
M.B., B.Ch., B.A.O., M.R.C.G.P., M.F.Hom.,
The Fourth Floor Flat, 86 Harley Street,
London W1N 1AE
Telephone: 071-580 4188

Joan Szinay, B.A., L.C.H., M.H.M.A. (U.K.) **081-449 3626**
Violet Hill Studios **071 624 6101**

Jane Wood, B.A., D.S.H., R.S.Hom., 27 Queen's Avenue, Finchley **081-346 2939**

The College of Homoeopathy Teaching Clinics
071-487 7416 / 081 852 0573
See 'Courses' for further information

HOMOEOPATHY

Dr. Brian Kaplan MBBCh MFHom
Homoeopathic Physician
136 Harley Street, London W1N 1AH
Telephone: 071-487 3416

Helen Austerberry, B.Sc., Homoeopath L.C.H., The South
London Natural Health Centre   071-720 8817

Jean Hanson, Homoeopath, C.Q.S.W., L.C.H., The South
London Natural Health Centre   071-720 8817

The Nutri Centre: Specialists in Vitamin & Nutritional
supplements including practitioners products. 7 Park Crescent,
London W1N 3HE   071 436 5122 FAX 071-436 5171

LOTHIAN

Dr Brian McMullen, BSc, MCCHB, DRCOG
031-551 5091

Dr Nicola Geddes MB, ChB, MSc(Nutrition) MFHom
031-551 5091

MERSEYSIDE

H. Simpson, D.O., N.C.S.O., M.G.O.(Lon.), M.I.C.A.K.,
M.R.S.H., M.H.P.A., M.A.A., M.C.K.O.R.E.   0744 88 3737

SHROPSHIRE

UNICORN HEALTH CENTRE
Panners, Wyle Cop, Shropshire SY1 1XB
Tel: 0743 357076

SHREWSBURY NATURAL HEALTH CENTRE
4 Radbrook Professional Centre, Banks Farm Road,
Shropshire SY3 6DU
Tel: 0743 248878

LLANIDLOES NATURAL HEALTH CENTRE
3 Victoria House, Victoria Terrace, Llanidloes,
Powys SY18 6BL
Tel: 05512 2230

SADDLERS HOUSE
Princes Street, Montgomery, Powys SY15 6PY
Tel: 0686 668753

SOMERSET

Complementary Medicine Centre, 9 Corporation Street,
Taunton, Somerset TA1 4AJ   0823 325022
or Redgate Medical Centre, Westonsoyland, Bridgwater,
Somerset TA6 5BF 0278 444411

STAFFORDSHIRE

Jill Povey, B.Sc.(Hons.), L.N.W.C.H., R.S.Hom., Leek Natural
Therapy Centre   0538 385346

L. Foulkes, B.A.Hons., R.S.Hom.
Newcastle Homoeopathic Practice
18 Water Street, Newcastle, Staffs
Tel: 0782 615184

HOMOEOPATHY

STRATHCLYDE

Dr. Robin G. Gibson, M.B., F.R.C.P., D.C.H., B.D.S., F.F.H.O.M.,
354 Albert Drive, Glasgow, G41 5PJ   041-427 1505

SOUTH YORKSHIRE

ANGELA NEEDHAM, M.A., M.C.H., R.S.H.O.M.
Homoeopath
The safe form of medicine for the future.
2 Prospect House, 295 City Road, Sheffield S2 5HH
Clinics on Monday, Tuesday and Thursday
Flexible Fees.
Enquiries, appointments Tel 0742 759136

HYPNOTHERAPY

Hypnosis is a state of relaxation during which the subconscious, which controls all the automatic processes and reactions, becomes more susceptible to suggestion.
Hypnotherapy is the use of Hypnosis to attempt alleviation of symptoms.
Curative Hypnotherapy is the use of this relaxation to uncover the individual cause of any problem and, by correcting this, ensuring a complete and permanent cure.
Association of Qualified
   Curative Hypnotherapists
Tel: 021-441 1775

HYPNOTHERAPY

There are many techniques used by the psychotherapist and of these, hypnosis is one of the most valuable. Not only does the body relax in the hypnotic state but the barrier or filter that normally controls the flow of information to and from the unconscious mind is also relaxed.

This relaxation allows the patient to begin the process of beneficial change by accepting a more positive approach to life and by developing within themselves more confidence and self-esteem.

At the same time, the therapist can give the patient the opportunity to explore traumatic events which may have occurred in the past, release the pain and unhappiness associated with them and in so doing, remove the emotional blocks that they have found so restricting to their enjoyment of life.

Donald M. Harrison, B.A.(Hons.Psych.), B.Sc.
National Association of Hypnotists
   & Psychotherapists,
Aberystwyth, Dyfed SY23 4EY
Tel: 09747 376

HYPNOSIS

Hypnosis has been practised throughout recorded history under a variety of names. The Austrian physician, Franz Anton Mesmer, is usually associated with its modern applications. His unacceptable theory (animal magnetism) and bizarre behaviour discredited "Mesmerism" in Europe in the late 18th Century. Attempts to revive its use in medicine and surgery in 19th Century Britain were stifled by a hostile medical establishment and the emergence of the drugs industry. (Although it has now been introduced into the curriculum of the Royal College of Nursing.)

Currently its most prevalent application is psychological. Hypnotherapy is a species of psychotherapy using hypnosis to facilitate and expedite any given treatment strategy. Hypnosis produces an absorbed state of mind (usually induced by the therapist's simply suggesting that the subject will allow him/herself to feel (relaxed) – characterised by such phenomena as heightened imagery, recall and concentration. This aids the delivery of any technique intended to change inappropriate thought, feeling or behaviour, or to counter undesirable physical manifestations of psychological origin.

P.J.D. Savage – Principal
The National College of Hypnosis and
   Psychotherapy,
12 Cross Street, Nelson, Lancashire BB9 7EN
Tel: 0282 699378

This article is intended to allay some of the fears concerning the use of Hypnosis, the myths and mystery surrounding which are totally undeserved, and to make clear that what takes place is very normal and non-magical, with predictable results.

There is absolutely no question of being controlled or manipulated, or even induced into a deep trance state. A person in Hypnosis (often referred to as Conscious Hypnosis) is not 'asleep' – they are often more aware of what is taking place than usual and their senses function more efficiently than normal. Nobody could possibly be made to do anything that they did not want to do, and anybody (except the truly mentally sub-normal, very young children and inebriates) can enter the hypnotic state. People who say or think, 'Nobody could get me under', or 'I wouldn't want anybody controlling my mind', or 'I might blurt my secrets out', are really demonstrating that they have a total misconception of what hypnosis really is.

The state of Hypnosis, a totally natural phenomenon, is most pleasant and particularly relaxing, and a person can converse quite easily whilst within the state. It is inconceivable that any harm could befall them. Indeed, the centuries old technique of

HYPNOTHERAPY

hypnosis is being used increasingly as an adjunct to orthodox medicine where it is proving a valuable alternative to drugs for anaesthesia, to accelerate healing, relieve stress and control pain. A good definition of Hypnosis is: 'A state of relaxation and concentration at one with a state of heightened awareness induced by suggestion'.

Your Therapist will use his or her voice to induce you into the state of Hypnosis and, although you are unlikely to feel 'hypnotised' as such, you will probably experience a feeling of mental and physical relaxation and your memory may well be enhanced. You will find your Therapist to be a caring professional person totally devoid of any mystical or magical powers! No flowing robes or swinging watches – just a reassuring manner to put you at ease, and the expertise to help you with your problem.

QUESTIONS AND ANSWERS

What is Hypnosis? A state of relaxation and concentration at one with a state of heightened awareness induced by suggestion. It is a non-addictive power for good and is a natural manifestation of the mind at work.

Are there some people you cannot hypnotise? No. (Except mentally handicapped, although of course the degree varies from person to person.)

Are drugs or tablets used? No.

Shall I be aware of what is happening? Yes. The predominant feeling of most people is – "It didn't work for me – I never went under."

So I am not asleep then? No, you are simply extremely relaxed. This is why the technique is called "Conscious Hypnosis".

Is there any cause at all for concern? None whatsover, Hypnosis is a proven therapeutic aid.

How many visits will I need? Simpler problems, like smoking, nailbiting, slimming, pre-test nerves, etc. usually require 1–3 sessions and the success rate is surprisingly high. The more deep-rooted nervous disorders require 'analytical' rather than 'suggestion' therapy which usually consists of 8–12 weekly sessions.

Could I be influenced to do anything against my will or nature? No. In fact you would be shocked out of the hypnotic state immediately any such action was suggested to you.

Can "normal" people be psycho-analysed? Not only can be, but should be. For an insight into yourself, it has no equal.

Neil French
P.O. Box 180
Bournemouth BH3 7YR
Tel: 0202 311191

SOUND ADVICE

on Albert Smith Health Cassettes.

15 titles covering a wide range of commonly experienced emotional and physical problems.
The "sound advice" given on side one is based on the wide "real life" experience gained by Mr Smith in his busy private practice. His straightforward easy to follow approach is appreciated by his patients and the Cassettes are widely recommended by the medical profession. On side one he describes in depth the underlying reasons or  causes of the various problems, be they fears or phobias, habits or compulsions, depression or insecurity or other stress related problems such as migraine or insomnia.

HEALTH CASSETTES

By listening to side two you will be able to enter into a controlled state of deep "Self Relaxation" in which, unhindered by stress and self doubt you can use the power of positive thinking and find that you are no longer influenced by others or haunted by events from the past.
(Mr Smith is a member of the National Association of Hypnotists & Psychotherapists and the World Federation of Healing.)
He has broadcast on both T.V. and radio.

Please supply the following cassettes by return:

☐ STOP SMOKING ☐ LOSE WEIGHT ☐ OVERCOME STRESS ☑ OVERCOME P.M.T.
☐ OVERCOME FEAR OF FLYING☐ OVERCOME MIGRAINE ☐ STOP BITING NAILS
☐ OVERCOME PAIN ☐ OVERCOME ARTHRITIS ☐ OVERCOME FEAR OF FAILURE
☐ OVERCOME FEARS & PHOBIAS ☐ OVERCOME STOMACH PROBLEMS
☐ OVERCOME INSOMNIA ☐ OVERCOME DEPRESSION
☐ LOOK AFTER YOUR HEART

ACCESS / VISA Number   Expiry Date: _____   P.O. / Chq. Enclosed: ____

NAME: _____

ADDRESS: _____

£4.95
EACH
P & P FREE

BROCHURE ON REQUEST
To: ALBERT SMITH HEALTH CASSETTES
183 Frinton Road, Kirby Cross, Frinton-on-Sea, Essex CO13 0PA Tel: 0255 672031

HYPNOTHERAPY

CAMBRIDGESHIRE

SELF AWARENESS AND
SELF IMPROVEMENT FOR
MENTAL AND PHYSICAL
WELL BEING

HYPNOSIS and NLP

SPEAKER AVAILABLE FOR SOCIETIES
Headway Hypnotherapy
4 Market Hill, Huntingdon
Tel: 0480 432022

DEVON

Hypnotherapy/Psychotherapy Counselling. Contact
The Clinic, 37 St. Peter Street, Tiverton   0884 255990

DORSET

3 WELLINGTON ROAD, BOURNEMOUTH, DORSET
TELEPHONE 0202 658578 (24 hours)
BOWOOD HOUSE MEDICAL CENTRE
FREE INTRODUCTORY CONSULTATION
OLIVE BLACKBURN, M.I.A.H., (analytical hypnotherapy)

ESSEX

Clinical Hypnotherapy (Colchester)
Bernard Morris, M.I.A.H., D.H.P.
Stress, Anxiety, Phobias, Smoking Allergies, Weight
Control, Panic Attacks, Confidence, Insomnia
Telephone: 0206-853539 (anytime)

Harmony Hypnotherapy and Primary Cause Analysis
Lyn Evans, B.A., Dip.H.P.
Psychotherapist/Hypnotherapist
NATURAL THERAPY CENTRE
Free initial consultation
Telephone 0268 692442

YOUR PROBLEMS TREATED!!

SMOKING – SLIMMING
STRESS – PHOBIAS
MEMORY – CONFIDENCE
OVER 15 YEARS EXPERIENCE
DOCTORS RECOMMEND PEOPLE TO US
ENSURE YOU ALSO GET
PROFESSIONAL TREATMENT
(0708) 764740 / 071-637 3377
2A CROSS ROAD,   7 PARK CRESCENT,
ROMFORD RM7 8AT   LONDON W1N 3HE
HORMASJI L.M.N.C.P., N.R.H.P., M.A.A.E.H., D.H.P.

Life-Force Centre for natural well-being   0206 250071

Christina Howtone
Psychotherapist/Hypnotherapist, S.H.A.P., C.R.A.H.,
M.A.B.C.H., M.C.A.Hyp., Member of B.A.C.
Depression. Anxiety/Panic Attacks. Lack of Confidence,
Self Esteem. Phobias. Personal Problems.
Contact: **0708-373175**
139 Sevenoaks Close, Harold Hill, Romford, Essex RM3 7EF

Hypnosis **CAN HELP YOU !**
Problems with Phobias, obsessions, weight,
smoking, fears, anxiety, insomnia
Contact: **Sandra Davis,**
Adv.Dip., E.H.P., N.L.P.(B.H.R)
Integrated Therapies   0376 344989

Mrs I. P. Gale
C.H.P.(N.C.), N.R.H.P.(Assoc.)
For Hypnotherapy and Psychotherapy
Leander, 6a Ronald Drive, Rayleigh, Essex SS6 9EB
Tel: 0268 780801

Stuart Wetherell, D.H.P., M.A.P.T.
Hypnotherapist & Counsellor
Working with people · to help them. Over 17 years in helping
professions. Specialising in anxiety related problems; also habit
reform, relationships, performance, motivation etc. Member
British Register of Complementary Practitioners (Hyp).
Tel: 0245 262975

GWENT

DR JOHN M. PLOWMAN

Caerleon Centre of Hypnotherapy & Psychotherapy
Dr John M. Plowman, Ph.D., D.H.P.(N.C.), M.N.R.H.P.
Member of:
The National Register of Hypnotherapists & Psychotherapists,
The British Psychological Society
The National Assoc. of teachers in Further & Higher Education.
**STRESS • WEIGHT • SMOKING
PHOBIAS • SPORTS THERAPY
SELF GROWTH • EDUCATIONAL COUNSELLING**
For Confidential & Qualified Consultations
Tel: Newport (0633) 420 095
By appointment only
**22 Goldcroft Common
Caerleon, Gwent NP6 1NG**

HAMPSHIRE

Hypnotherapy, Psychotherapy, Counselling at The
Southsea Centre for Complementary Medicine   0705 874748
See our ad under Health Centres

HERTFORDSHIRE

You can become a Psychologist/Hypnotherapist (Diploma)
Finest individual Training available.
ACADEMY OF HYPNOTHERAPY
Principal: Harley St. Psychologist **P. J. Millin** P.H.C.
We have helped many hundreds to become Hypnotherapists
Telephone 081-441 9685

LEICESTERSHIRE

Dr. M. K. Arora, M.B.B.S., D.A.B., 4 Meadow Close, Wolvey,
Hinckley, Leicestershire   0455 220464 after 7.00pm

59

INTEGRAL PSYCHOANALYSIS

INTEGRAL PSYCHOANALYSIS METHOD
(School of Norberto Keppe)

Keppe's basic philosophy holds that the essence of the human being is real action, that is action based on goodness, beauty and truth. If we know the pathological attitudes that we have, which impede our being from manifesting itself, we can improve our existence tremendously. Human beings are endowed with reason but we act and think with our emotions, thus limiting our knowledge. With this dangerous habit all beauty and light in our lives is locked away. What is left is our unconscious attitude against living life intelligently.

The most common factor in all human pathology is the rejection of pure (good) action. This manifests itself not only in bodily disease, but also in a decrease in intelligence, and the destruction of a loving attitude. If this rejection is conscientised it can liberate all the capacities that we have, allowing us to live fulfilling and happy lives.

Centre of Integral Psychoanalysis
(Analytical Trilogy) Ltd
6 Colville Road, London W11 2BP
Tel: 071 727 4404

IRIDOLOGY

Iridology is an excellent way of analysing your health. It is based on genetic markings, colourings and pigmentations of the iris of the eye and, like fingerprints they are totally unique to the individual. A well-trained Iridologist, who uses either R.Ir., or M.S.Ir., after their name, looks into each eye with a magnifying glass and torch before discussing potential trouble spots with you. Iridology is safe, painless and non-invasive, and once finding out your weak areas by working with the British Iris Chart, the practitioner will give advice on a treatment programme if necessary.

The British Society of Iridologists is the regulating body for all Iridologists in Great Britain and provide a variety of services including a List of Registered Practitioners covering most areas in the U.K., training courses, book lists and seminars.

Sheelagh Colton
The British Society of Iridologists
40 Stokewood Road, Bournemouth BH3 7NE
Tel: 0202 518078

British School of Iridology
Dolfin House, 6 Gold Street
Saffron Walden, Essex CB10 1EJ
Tel: 0799 26138

National Council & Register of Iridologists
80 Portland Road, Bournemouth BH9 1NQ

Federation of Iridologists Association of professionally qualified Iridologists providing information to the public about Iridology and maintains a referral list of members in the UK with international links   0963 70300 OR 081-874 8882

DERBYSHIRE

Margaret Pardoe, R.Ir., M.H., S.R.N., S.C.M., Natural Choice Therapy Centre, 24 St. John Street, Ashbourne, Derbyshire DE6 1GH   0335 46096

HAMPSHIRE

Gwen Crowe, R.Ir.   0252 616751
see under Touch for Health

LONDON

Loekie Bone
Traditional Iridology & Rayid Homoeopathy, Kinesiology, Iris Photography
★ *Stockists of 'Gifting Your Child' tapes* ★
67 Melrose Road, Southfields, London SW18 1PG
Telephone 081-874 8882
South London Natural Health Centre,
4a Clapham Common, Southside, London SW4
Telephone 081-720 8817

SOMERSET

Complementary Medicine Centre, 9 Corporation Street, Taunton, Somerset TA1 4AJ   0823 325022

KINESIOLOGY

APPLIED KINESIOLOGY

Kinesiology uses a combination of concepts and techniques drawn from Acupuncture, Chiropractic, Massage, Nutrition, Osteopathy, Shiatsu and others. Being eclectic in approach, it forms a very useful "toolkit" for practitioners of all types to use in conjunction with their other skills.

Kinesiology uses simple muscle tests to analyse functional imbalances in the body; and touch, acupressure massage, and nutritional support to resolve them.

The phenomenon of Kinesiology was discovered in 1964 by Dr. George Goodheart, D.C. a chiropractor. He found that by testing muscles, and correcting those functioning below par with firm massage on the origin and insertion, the results were instantaneous.

Research showed that other types of reflexes could be used to strengthen muscles and balance organ energy, enhance blood flow, and stimulate the lymphatic system. When the meridians of acupuncture were correlated to the muscles, this created a breakthrough which led to a much greater understanding of physiological functions, their electromagnetic control circuits and bio-computer functions.

Learning basic Kinesiology is simple. Some highly trained professionals say they learned more usable techniques in a two day class than they did in two years of formal study. The preventive and therapeutic power of Kinesiology is destined to make it a universal indispensable tool in health care.

Brian H. Butler
The Association for Systematic Kinesiology
39 Browns Road
Surbiton, Surrey KT5 8ST
Tel: 081-399 3215

HOLISTIC KINESIOLOGY

Holistic Kinesiology is a simple and effective way to balance and restore our natural energies. It combines modern understandings about movement and the nervous system with the ancient wisdoms of Chinese medicine.

The art of gently testing muscle responses identifies energy blocks and imbalances. Reflex and acupressure stimulation together with subtle and specific massage techniques release the blocks and restore balance.

By the same method, the effectiveness of treatment is assessed and awareness is developed of the instinctive body knowledge. A two way communication is established through the muscle responses, accurately reflecting the subtlest of changes in the nervous system and enabling highly individualised treatments.

The treatment is called "balancing" and works on whichever level – physical, emotional, biochemical or subtle – is indicated by the body's own responses.

(**Touch for Health** is the name given to the foundation training. It is taught over three weekends and is open to anyone. There are then various options for advanced and professional training.)

Adrian Voce
Kinesiology School, 67 Muswell Hill
London N10 3PN
Tel: 081-883 3799

BEDFORDSHIRE

KINESIOLOGY

KINESIOLOGY
(MUSCLE TESTING & ENERGY BALANCING)
FOR
BALANCED HEALTH
NEW SELF-HELP MANUAL
CLASS TEXTBOOK, 144 PAGES, HUNDREDS OF
PICTURES, PACKED WITH TECHNIQUES, IDEAL FOR
LAY PEOPLE & PROFESSIONALS. *£20 + £3 p&p*
For details of classes and Certificate Courses, S.A.E.
The Academy of Systematic Kinesiology
39, BROWNS ROAD, SURBITON, SURREY, KT5 8ST

LIGHT THERAPY

S.A.D.
SAD stands for Seasonal Affective Disorder or Winter Depression, affecting about 10 million people in Britain in varying degrees. It is associated with a biochemical imbalance in the hypothalamus due to the lack of bright light in winter.

SYMPTOMS
The symptoms of SAD start each winter and cease in spring. Sufferers may have to endure oversleeping, lack of energy, unhappiness, mood changes, loss of libido, and carbohydrate craving and overeating.

TREATMENT
There are 5 NHS clinics specialising in SAD. They routinely use light therapy, finding it effective in up to 85% of diagnosed cases. Light therapy usually means bright light treatment (at least 5 times brighter than normal office lighting), which replaces the missing sunlight, by using a light box or head-worn light visor every day. A new development is Dawn Simulation, which regulates the body clock by providing an artificial gradual dawn light in the morning.

OTHER APPLICATIONS
Research is taking place into other body clock related problems such as night shift, jet lag and P.M.S.

SUPPORT
The SAD Association has an extensive national support network. They can be contacted at PO Box 989, London SW7 2PZ.

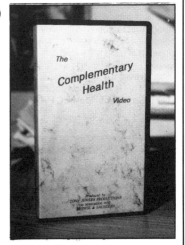

MACROBIOTICS

Macrobiotics is a way of eating based on research into what the world's most healthy societies eat. By eating a diet high in complex carbohydrates, low in saturated fats, and low in simple refined sugars these societies enjoy a long life with an extremely low incidence of heart disease, cancer and other common illnesses. Grains, beans and vegetables, all staples of a macrobiotic diet, are recommended as good sources of complex carbohydrates. Most people eating a macrobiotic diet eat very little or no meat, dairy food or eggs. These high fat foods are replaced with fish, beans, humus, tofu, nuts seeds and other more healthy ingredients all low in saturated fats. In addition, people eating a macrobiotic diet use fruits, malts and other naturally sweet foods to create a sweet taste rather than suffer the harmful effects of refined sugar.

The value of this approach has been confirmed by the World Health Organisation who in 1989 published their report Diet Nutrition And The Prevention Of Chronic Diseases. The evidence overwhelmingly proved that this type of diet greatly reduced the incidence of heart disease, cancer, diabetes and many other common serious illnesses.

In the end macrobiotics is all about giving your body exactly what you need and therefore each individual eats their own unique style of macrobiotics depending on their lifestyle. For anyone starting macrobiotics to recover from a health problem, advice from an experienced macrobiotic counsellor is recommended.

Simon Brown
Community Health Foundation
188 Old Street, London EC1V 98P
Tel: 071-251 4076

DEVON

Oliver Cowmeadow, B.Sc., P.G.C.E., M.R.S.S.,

Personal dietary Health consultations and shiatsu treatments for a wide range of specific problems and advice on increasing health. Appointments in Totnes and Exeter. The Coach House, Buckyette Farm, Littlehempston, Totnes, Devon. TQ9 6ND. Tel: (0803) 762593.

LONDON

The East-West Restaurant

"London's finest wholefood/macrobiotic restaurant. Open seven days for hot meals (from £4.50) salads & sugar-free desserts."

188 Old Street, London.   Tel: 081-608 0300

MAGNETIC THERAPY

Considered from a purely physical point of view, electromagnetism is the primary force that mediates all interactions within living systems. There are said to be 100,000 highly integrated, intermolecular reactions per cell per second – all involving electromagnetism in one way or another.

Magnetic therapy attempts to interact with human physiology, stimulating the body's natural balancing processes through their electromagnetic aspects. Some forms of this therapy rely entirely on the polarity which exists in all of nature. Others use finely tuned magnets to interact with the acupuncture points. The science is still in its infancy, but holds out great hope for the future.

John H. Davidson, M.A.(Cantab)
Wholistic Research Company, Bright Haven
Robin's Lane, Lolworth, Cambridge CB3 8HH
Tel: 0954 781074

MASSAGE

MASSAGE – A HEALING ART

Massage has been practised in various ways in many cultures for thousands of years.

Massage can be a pleasure both to receive and to give.

It can soothe, heal, invigorate and tone. It helps tired muscles to rest and tight overworked muscles to relax. Massage doesn't only work on the body. Having a massage can benefit body, mind, and spirit. The touch and movement of the practitioner's hands helps to relax while this same touch and movement induces deeper breathing and greater peace. This can lessen the symptoms of stress and promote better functioning of the immune system through the healing quality of positive touch.

The Secretary
Association of Massage Practitioners
101 Bounds Green Road
London N22 4DF

Association of Massage Practitioners

A professional organisation setting standards for Holistic Massage. New Practitioners gain support and supervision opportunities and Registered Members – listing to the public. *Contact the Secretary,* **A.M.P., 101 Bounds Green Road, London N22 4DF**

MASSAGE

Most forms of traditional western-style massage focus on manipulating by hand the body's soft tissues with movements that involve: pressing; kneading; moulding; friction; etc. These applications generally free up the soft tissues and improve elasticity, resulting in liberation from discomfort which allows for increased range and movement. Blood circulation is improved, nerves are soothed and all systems of the body generally benefit.

Regular massage can promote health and assist in the prevention of disease by encouraging removal of the body's waste products and harmful pollutants taken in with food, water and air which, left unattended, would become toxic. Cells threatened by the potentially damaging implications of these poisons, broadcast their anxiety throughout the organism, contributing to a harmful stress cycle.

Once massage begins to regulate the system, its enjoyable effects can release pleasure-forming endorphins thereby setting in motion a positive health cycle. The combined toning and relaxing nature of massage, tend to uplift the spirits while giving an overall sense of calmness.

Whilst skill is an essential part of massage, it is the equivalent of 'green fingers', intuition and the mysterious power of touch that can lead to massage becoming a profound healing experience.

Clive Chabrier: Principal
The West London School of
**   Therapeutic Massage**
Tel: 071-229 4672

INDIAN HEAD MASSAGE – THE MEHTA METHOD

The stress of modern living is nothing but a pain in the neck! and very few can boast immunity to it.

One treatment that is guaranteed to lift you out of the hustle and bustle of city life is Indian Head Massage. It includes massage of the neck, shoulder, scalp and face.

Head massage has been practised in India for over a thousand years. The technique was originally used by women who believed that massaging their heads with natural oils, kept their long hair in healthy and lustrous condition.

Head massage is an excellent treatment also for men. It helps to alleviate stress and tension; this is not only an invaluable treatment to maintain the best possible looks of the hair but also for stress-linked troubles such as headache, neck ache and eyestrain.

It soothes, comforts and rebalances energy flow, leaving you with a feeling of peace and well being. The sense of tranquility which head massage creates, has to be experienced to be believed.

Mr Narendra Mehta
136 Holloway Road, London N7 8DD
Tel: 071-609 3590

MASSAGE

ON-SITE MASSAGE

On-Site Massage (OSM) is an exciting form of modern bodywork which has been designed to be carried out in the workplace using a special portable chair.

Unlike conventional massage, On-Site Massage involves no disrobing, application of oils, and takes no longer than 20 minutes. This makes On-Site Massage convenient and non-invasive to receive. Using a wide range of acupressure techniques, clients are left feeling relaxed, calm, energised and clearly focused.

On-Site Massage has been featured on the BBC, MTV, and in various newspapers and magazines, and is becoming increasingly popular.

For bodyworkers, OSM represents a completely new service industry and an unprecedented opportunity to increase their income. For many individuals, On-Site Massage represents their first opportunity to experience any form of bodywork. Regular OSM helps to break up muscular tension, boost energy levels and keeps them supple and alert. helping to create a fitter, healthier and more productive workforce. Companies who have used On-Site Massage inclue The Body Shop International, The British Red Cross, The BBC, BP, and The Metropolitan Police.

For further details of professional training in On-Site Massage and our service, *Stressbusters* please contact the:

British School of On-Site Massage
Tel: 071-383 7943 or 071-916 3684
or write to:
The British School of On-Site Massage
48 Camden Street,
London NW1 0DX

BERKSHIRE

Rosemary School of Natural Therapy, 10 Pine Ridge, Newbury, Berkshire RG13 2NQ   0635 31678

CAMBRIDGESHIRE

Biodynamic Massage Training
1 year part-time course in Cambridge, Starts September
Details from **Gill Westland,** B.A., Dip.C.O.T., I.T.E.C.
8 Wetenhall Road, Cambridge CB1 3AG
Telephone 0223 214658

The British School of On-Site Massage

If you have been thinking about working with your hands, helping other people and also building a profitable career, then On-Site Massage may be the perfect vehicle for you.

The British School of On-Site Massage run regular courses around the UK in On-Site Massage techniques and protocol.

For more details of our comprehensive training for complete beginners or intensive training courses for qualified bodyworkers, call or write to:

The British School of On-Site Massage
48 Camden Street, London NW1 0DX.
071 916 3684 or **071 383 7943**

DERBYSHIRE

Christine Hudson, B.A., I.T.E.C., A.I.P.T.I., Natural Choice Therapy Centre, 24 St. John Street, Ashbourne, Derbyshire DE6 1GH   0335 46096

DEVON

Rosalind Lacey, I.T.E.C. Qualified Therapist, Remedial and Therapeutic Massage. Contact The Clinic, 37 St. Peter Street, Tiverton   0884 255990

ESSEX

Essex School of Massage
Principal: **Jacky Barrett**
Intensive course leading to professional
ITEC qualification. Small Classes.
For details telephone: **0992 892110**

66

MASSAGE

THE WEST LONDON SCHOOL OF THERAPEUTIC MASSAGE
071-229 4672

Stages are: Interview – 6 consecutive days of intensive tuition, Monday to Saturday. Regular Thursday evening attendances for as long as seems appropriate, plus home study of the course text book. Written and practical examinations in the presence of an "International Therapy Examination Council" examiner. For most students the course and examinations will be completed in around 3–4 months. Successful candidates will be awarded the I.T.E.C. Diploma in Massage, Anatomy and Physiology. Application may then be made to join I.P.T.I. This professional body offers amongst other benefits, suitable insurance cover at attractive rates.

POST GRADUATE STUDIES

The above professional qualification forms the foundation and prerequisite for a wider programme of study for graduates, that enables them to expand their knowledge and enlarge their skills in different ways, giving them the opportunity to follow their own chosen direction, whilst continuously gaining invaluable first-hand experience in the field.

SUBJECTS INCLUDE:

ADVANCED MASSAGE I, II + III
VITALISING MASSAGE
MASSAGE IN PREGNANCY
HOLISTIC MASSAGE
TRADITIONAL CHINESE MASSAGE
AROMATHERAPY
ACUPRESSURE

REFLEXOLOGY
SPORTS THERAPY
NUTRITIONAL COUNSELLING
BACH FLOWER REMEDIES
PSYCHO-PHYSICAL RELEASE
BODY CENTRED PSYCHOTHERAPY (WHICH
INCORPORATES REBIRTHING BODY WORK & DREAMCRAFT)

PLUS: Various Supportive Workshops, e.g., Anatomy From The Surface, practice Management Course, Diagnostic Skills and Pathology and First Aid For Therapists.

FOR MASSAGE, ANATOMY + PHYSIOLOGY LEAFLET, PHONE: 071-229 4672
THE WEST LONDON SCHOOL OF THERAPEUTIC MASSAGE,
41A ST. LUKE'S ROAD, LONDON W11 1DD

MASSAGE

SHIATSU MASSAGE
Treat the nervous system . . .
Soothing and healing to mind and body.
Teresa Deeming, Qualified Therapist
45 St John Road, Clacton CO15 4BT
Tel: (0225) 474331
Also Training Available

GLOUCESTER

Valerie Johnston, D.E.A.S., I.T.E.C., L.T.Phys., M.I.P.T.I.
offers therapeutic remedial treatments   0242 224283

HAMPSHIRE

Alison Perrott, S.P.Dip.A., M.I.S.P.A., M.I.S.M.A., M.A.S.K.,
M.T.M.I., The S.E.E.D. Institute, 10 Magnolia Way, Fleet, Hants
GU13 9JZ   0252 626448
See our Ad under Courses & Tuition

Christopher G. Ockendon, M.I.S.P.A., I.T.E.C., Remedial
Massage, Aromatherapy, Reflexology, Naturopath, The Lowford
Clinic, Southampton   0703 404445

HERTFORDSHIRE

Su Hagan, S.P.Dip.A., M.I.S.P.A., M.T.M.I., The S.E.E.D.
Institute, Stable Flat, Serge Hill Road, Bedmond, Abbots Langley,
Herts WD5 0RY   0923 268898
See our Ad under Courses & Tuition

LONDON

Vicky Hamilton, Holistic Massage, I.T.E.C., The South London
Natural Health Centre   071-720 8817

Naomi Kemeny, Holistic Massage, I.T.E.C., The South
London Natural Health Centre   071-720 8817

Nathalé Mineau, Holistic Massage, I.T.E.C., The South
London Natural Health Centre   071-720 8817

Relaxing Therapeutic Massage by
Qualified Therapist
Marea Young-Taylor, I.T.E.C., A.I.P.T.I.
Central London 071-262 1426

The Community Health Foundation
runs massage courses that lead to an ITEC certificate.
The course consists of 3 hours tuition per week (12 weeks). Cost £295
Price inclusive of exam fees.
Call 071-251 4076 for details

Georgina Tisdall, Holistic Massage, I.T.E.C., The South
London Natural Health Centre   071-720 8817

Sheila Dainow, D.C.S., D.T.M., M.S.H.P.
Therapeutic Massage Practitioner in North London
For Details/Appointments **081-368 3605**
Holistic Treatment for Stress Symptoms & Chronic Tension

 Biodynamic Massage Training
4 term part-time course commencing September in
West London leading to a Basic Biodynamic Massage Certificate.
Apply: **Chiron Centre for Holistic Psychotherapy**
26 Eaton Rise, Ealing, London W5 2QB
Tel: 081-997 5219

LOTHIAN

Maggie Burt, Dip.T.M., S.H.P., DipAroma, E.S.N.T., Therapeutic Massage   031-551 5091

NOTTINGHAMSHIRE

GREATER MANCHESTER

MASSAGE

OXFORDSHIRE

WHITE HORSE SCHOOL OF MASSAGE AND NATURAL THERAPIES

For ITEC accredited courses in MASSAGE, ANATOMY, PHYSIOLOGY + RELATED THERAPIES
The stepping stone to a career as an Alternative and/or Physical Therapist. Weekend or weekday courses and workshops available, small numbers to ensure personal attention.
Telephone for prospectus: Oxfordshire (0235; 847571 or write to:
36 Barretts Way, Sutton Courtenay, Oxfordshire OX14 4DE

SOMERSET

Complementary Medicine Centre, 9 Corporation Street, Taunton, Somerset TA1 4AJ 0823 325022

June Markham, S.P.Dip.A., M.I.S.P.A., The S.E.E.D. Institute, 93A Ilchester Road, Yeovil, Somerset BA21 3BJ 0935 74379
See our Ad under Courses & Tuition

STAFFORDSHIRE

Eva Ryback-Coare, L.C.S.P. Assoc., Leek Natural Therapy Centre 0538 360999

Linda J. Skellam, Leek Natural Therapy Centre 0538 383726

SUFFOLK

Remedial Massage For Women
Susan Wolsten-Croft, I.T.E.C., M.T.I.G.B.
Massage, including Indian Head, in your own home.
Telephone: **Bures (0787) 228594** for appointments

Rachel Stanford, L.C.S.P.(Assoc.), Remedial Massage, Eye, Suffolk 0379 870 938

SURREY

Farnham Holistic Centre, Tilford Road, Farnham, Surrey GU9 8HU 0252 734445

SUSSEX

The Floatarium, 21 Bond Street, Brighton BN1 1RD 0273 679555
Fax: 0273 601 992

EAST SUSSEX

Rosebay House, Eastbourne 0323 503211

YORKSHIRE

Enrico Dodson, L.C.S.P.(Assoc.), M.I.I.R., M.B.S.A.M., 21 Cowlersley Lane, Huddersfield HD4 5TY 0484 641982

CONNECTIVE TISSUE MASSAGE

CTM, Connective Tissue Massage and it's advanced form of STM, Soft Tissue Mobilisation are both based on ancient techniques upgraded and carried forward into the modern era. They have strongly alterative effects on the body, where they alter the state of nerves and release restrictions in body membranes and muscle sheaths. Similarly, their correct use restores joint mobility and change the flow pattern of blood and lymph.

When used in appropriate areas, CTM materially alters the function of inner organs and their secretions. STM releasing changes the blood flow within the cranium, producing a de-stressing effect on the mind. Both are used to prepare the patient for spinal, cranial or joint manipulation.

Both are used in dance and sports injuries, when they cut treatment times. These advanced forms of hand technique have deep and far reaching uses as true bio-dynamic therapies in beauty care.

CTM and STM are well acclaimed by patients for their beneficial effects, but, because of their very precise nature students have to undergo most rigorous training to 3 or more levels of competence over 2 or more years of study and practise.

For further information contact
Terence Slocombe, Director
European College of Therapies
Tel: 071-495 3995 Fax: 071-495 4214

MEDICAL DOWSING
(OR RADIESTHESIA)

While dowsing is best known in association with seeking water, the use of the faculty is also becoming well known for its application to the healing arts. In this connection dowsing is sometimes referred to as radiesthesia.

Not only is a thorough knowledge of the alternative therapy you are using essential but an in-depth ability of using the pendulum accurately is of paramount importance, too. Many alternative therapists use the dowsing function alongside their method of treating ill health which gives them an insight into their patient they would not normally have had. It can take them back to the cause of their patients' illnesses rather than treating the symptoms alone. Dowsing can be used with the patient or at a distance using a witness such as a blood spot or hair sample. It can be used to determine which therapy is most suitable, which remedy, its potency and duration of application to give but a few examples. Some doctors and dentists have found it such a valuable tool that they use it daily in their practices.

Part of the British Society of Dowsers' function is to provide lectures and courses in this art. Further details can be obtained by sending an SAE to:

Sycamore Barn, Hastingleigh,
Ashford, Kent TN25 5HW
Tel: 0233 750253

The British Society of Dowsers
S.A.E. to Sycamore Barn, Hastingleigh,
Ashford, Kent TN25 5HW
for details of membership, lectures,
courses and congresses.

MEDITATION

To benefit fully from meditation, it must be practised wholeheartedly and regularly. This brings peace of mind and relaxation; worries and anxieties decrease and there is a better sense of proportion. Efficiency and confidence increase, relationships are often easier and life seems more purposeful and to have real direction.

Scientific experiments carried out on people meditating have found a general reduction in the rate of breathing and a slower heartbeat. The basal metabolic rate decreases by as much as 40% and an increase in the alpha rhythm of brain impulses indicates a state of deep rest, more profound than that of sleep or hypnosis – but all with an inner alertness.

There is a growing awareness of strength within the individual which is always there and is totally dependable. The regular meditator also begins to see, more and more clearly, how differences are superficial and that beneath the surface there is unity and wholeness.

The School of Meditation
158 Holland Park Avenue, London W11 4UH
Tel: 071-603 6116

MEDITATION

MEGAVITAMIN THERAPY

Both scurvy and beri-beri are examples of overt vitamin deficiency diseases. Recommended Daily Allowances (RDA's) or Recommended Nutrient Intakes (RNI's), are levels of nutrients marginally above that known to prevent such diseases. However, there is a wide concept difference between preventing overt vitamin deficiency diseases and promoting optimum health. Megavitamin Therapy attempts to provide each cell of the body with the correct levels of nutrients to promote optimum function and longevity. People are individually assessed on the premise that their needs will vary according to their current diet, lifestyle, level of exercise and exposure to pollution. Megavitamin Therapy is most commonly and effectively used in conjunction with Nutrition Therapy.

Kate Neil: Nutrition Consultant
The Institute For Optimum Nutrition
5 Jerdan Place, London SW6 1BE
Tel: 071-385 7984

LONDON

The Nutri Centre, Specialists in Vitamin and Nutritional Supplements including Practioners Products, 7 Park Crescent, London W1N 3HE   071-436 5122 FAX 071-436 5171

METAMORPHIC TECHNIQUE

The Metamorphic Technique is a simple approach to self-healing and transformation which can happen in a natural, unconscious and spontaneous way as we witness in nature. Two conditions are necessary: energy (the seed, caterpillar, sperm and ovum must be alive for transformation to happen), and a propitious environment. As with the soil and moisture for the seed, the Metamorphic practitioner acts as a catalyst and the energy, the power of life within the recipient takes over and does the work of transformation, of metamorphosis, from who one is to who one can be.

A light touch is used on the spinal reflexes in the feet, hands and head which we have found to correspond to the time before birth, to the development of the embryo and foetus from conception onward, a time when we established all our physical, mental, emotional and behavioural characteristics which of course affect the way we conduct our life now. The Metamorphic Technique helps reveal these basic prenatal patterns and the power of life within the person acts to release the energy locked in them. There is healing, transformation.

Because of its simplicity and the fact that a session is very pleasant and relaxing, many people are happy to use this technique every week as a tool for transformation of their difficulties and realisation of their potential.
Courses are given at the Metamorphic Association's Headquarters:

67 Ritherdon Road, London SW17 8QE
Tel: 081-672 5951
Please write or telephone for the full programme of activities. Publications also available.

DERBYSHIRE

Maureen Muschamp, Natural Choice Therapy Centre, 24 St. John Street, Ashbourne, Derbyshire DE6 1GH   0333 46096

ESSEX

Great Clacton Natural Healing Centre. 6 St Johns Road, Great Clacton, Essex   0255 436059

MUSIC, VOICE AND SOUND

SOUND MIND, SOUND BODY

One of the ways human beings have always kept themselves healthy and in tune has been by singing and chanting together with other members of their community. This served not only a spiritual purpose but also a physical, emotional and a psychic one. At the same time people were able to tune themselves with their family and other members of their society, creating societal harmony and a common purpose. By doing this in the name of the divine, both the individual and community were tuned to the spiritual dimension. These two alone would be considered by most traditional peoples, the most important activities of daily life. But fulfilling these goals by chanting together, other essential needs are also met. Because our physical bodies are composed of a multitude of different and complex resonances, from the heart beat, brain rhythms, organ, protein, molecule and atomic resonances, to name but a few, the most effective way of keeping all these in tune with all others, is by using sound. While all sound is powerful, perhaps the most powerful sound of all for the human being is his or her own, namely that of the most magical of instruments, the human voice. Likewise in the emotional realm – imagine trying to remain sad while singing. It is not possible. Lastly, psychically and energetically the voice plays an essential role. The Tibetans tell us that the human being has three bodies: body, voice and mind. In other words, it has a physical and a spiritual dimension and in between is the voice and breath. The voice is uniquely able to put our physical and non physical parts of ourselves into harmony with each other.

In the last fifty years the modern industrialized West has become disaffected with its own religious tradition, leaving only a tiny proportion of its population still participating in any kind of spiritual practice. At the same time it has left our society voiceless, without any practice of sonic healing that would normally be a natural part of everyday life.

In the last few years myself and others have studied these traditional ways and have brought back opportunities for people once again to come into tune with themselves, their society and the divine by liberating their voices and their inner selves in a joyous and heaing experience using sound. This work is available to those who feel they are not musical, or 'cannot sing', as much as to professional musicians. Such work with sound can be intense and moving. After participating, some have said that dark clouds that have long affected their lives have lifted. Others have found that nagging fears and pains, both physical and emotional, have disappeared and they have been healed. Many have come away with the means at their disposal to harmonize their everyday lives in totally new ways and have reported a new found joy in being alive and relating to others.

Jill Purce, The Healing and Magical Voice
Sacred, overtone and shamanic
chanting workshops
Contact: Inner Sound, Garden Flat
9 Yonge Park, London N4 3NU
Tel: (071) 607 5819

CUMBRIA

Voice-Work: Esoteric sound, S. Lakeland Music Therapy Centre   05395 32875

HAMPSHIRE

LONDON

Courses for Communication Skills and Voice, singing with the Alexander Technique, Alan Mars, 137 Grosvenor Avenue, London N5 2NH   071-226 5805

NATURAL BEAUTY

Skin care products which can be described as "Natural" are made from plant ingredients and the higher the proportion of plant the better. As the skin has a fluid structure which is acid, fruit acids combined with other plant substances are the best. As we grow older skin cell renewal slows down and the build-up of dead cells makes the complexion look dull. By stimulating the acid mantle with refined fruit juices, dead skin cells are gently removed daily to reveal the healthy functioning skin beneath. Cell renewal is achieved by cleansing and also nusing whole plant moisturising and treatment creams to nourish and protect skin's own moisture and protein content. Good plant products have a holistic healing affect on the body's most protective mantle to create a total healthy glow.

For further information contact:
Katie May,
Yin Yang, James Barn Farm,
Naunton, Nr. Cheltenham,
Gloucestershire
Tel: 0451 850787.
Fax: 0451 850512

NATURAL BEAUTY

FOREVER LIVING PRODUCTS

F.L.P. market a complete range of PURE ALOE VERA products

ALOE VERA has been known for thousands of years for its wide-ranging healing properties and has been called various names, including the "FIRST AID PLANT" the "MIRACLE PLANT" and the "PLANT OF IMMORTALITY".

For Help with Arthritis, Rheumatism, Colitis, Liver and Kidney disorders, Migraine, Eczema, Psoriasis, ulcers, Ear, Eye and Throat infections, Hay Fever and all Allergies, Cuts, Burns, Sprains and Much More.

ALL PRODUCTS ARE 100% NATURAL WITH A 90 DAY MONEY-BACK GUARANTEE
TRY THE WORLD'S PUREST ALOE VERA PRODUCTS WITH NO SIDE EFFECTS

For more information contact:

EAST ANGLIA & THE SOUTH
MIKE & JAN ROBINSON
Tel: 0206 230707

MIDLANDS & THE NORTH
CHARLES & MARG GRIFFIN
Tel: 0889 583256

DISTRIBUTORS REQUIRED IN ALL AREAS

NATUROPATHY

Naturopathic Medicine (Naturopathy) is a separate and distinct form of medicine, having its own philosophy and methods of treatment. It is based on the unalterable principle that ONLY NATURE HEALS and it is within the individual's ability to restore health.

The principles of Naturopathy are:

1) Given the appropriate opportunity, nature will heal.
2) Correct food is the only medicine that the body requires.
3) Dis-ease is an attempt to heal by elimination.
4) All disease has the same common causation.

In practice Naturopathy recognises that the stress of twentieth century living degrades the life force and various factors affect the body's ability to restore maximum health. These include chemical imbalance, structural or mechanical distortions and psychological stress. In order to treat the patient successfully, Naturopaths will always treat the patient as a whole and never attempt to merely alleviate the symptoms.

The British College of Naturopathy and Osteopathy offers an Honours degree on Osteopathy and a Diploma in Naturopathy. Graduates are eligible to apply for membership of the General Council and Register of Naturopaths, which is the regulatory body for qualified and Registered Naturopaths in the United Kingdom.

To find your local Registered Naturopath, contact the General Council and Register of Naturopaths, **6 Netherhall Gardens, London NW3 5RR Tel: 071 435 7830**

British Register of Naturopaths
1 Albemarle Road, York YO2 1EN

British College of Naturopathy and Osteopathy
Frazer House, 6 Netherall Gardens
Hampstead, London NW3 5RR
Tel: 071-435 7830 (clinic), 071-435 6464 (college)

LONDON

The Nutri Centre, Specialists in Vitamin & Nutritional Supplements including Practitioners Products. 7 Park Crescent, London W1N 3HE   071-436 5122 FAX 071-436 5171

75

NEURO-LINGUISTIC PROGRAMMING

Usually referred to as NLP, this discipline originated from experiential research in the skills and techniques used by three leading psychotherapists, Fritz Perls (Gestalt Therapy), Virginia Satir (Family Therapy), and Milton Erickson (Hypnotherapy).

This process of modelling the intuitive skills of outstanding therapists has led to the development of a comprehensive range of client-centred skills and techniques for producing empowering changes in behaviours, capabilities or beliefs that are probably the most effective available. As an example, the desensitisation of a phobia can often be completed and tested in as little as 10 or 15 minutes using the phobia cure process.

The theoretical roots of NLP are profound, being based in applied systems thinking, linguistics, neurology and body language, however the basic idea is simple. Experience is constructed. Once you know how experience is made up, it is a lot easier to help people make it up more the way they would like it to be.

Because of the effectiveness of NLP skills in a wide range of applications, the field has grown very rapidly within health care. To find out more about NLP, read Britain's best-selling NLP book "Introducing Neuro-Linguistic Programming" by Joseph O'Connor and John Seymour.

John Seymour Associates
17 Boyce Drive
St Werberghs
Bristol B52 9XQ
Tel: 0272 557827

Association for Neuro-Linguistic Programming
100b Carysfort Road, London NI6 9AP
Tel: 071-241 3664

NEURO-LINGUISTIC PROGRAMMING

ppd - nlp

Neuro-Linguistic Programming offers probably the most powerful communication and personal development skills available in the fields of management, psychotherapy and education.

We are the UK's major NLP organisation and work closely with the founder, John Grinder. We use the top international trainers and offer free follow-up coaching days on completion of basic training. Our long-established Foundation Skills course teaches the achievement of goals through deep rapport and high quality communication techniques - the ability to know what you want and how to get it.

Come and learn more about us at our free introductory evenings held every month in Central London. Call us for details on **071-794 0960.**

Pace Personal Development

NUTRITIONAL THERAPY

Modern Nutritional Therapy assesses each person individually, taking a wide spectrum of factors into account. These include, family history, diet, exercise, pollution, anti-nutrients and stress. The aim is to provide an individually assessed dietary and nutritional supplement programme that the person can competently participate in, that will, over time, move them towards an optimum state of health. The goal of Nutrition Therapy is to empower the individual to become motivated, responsible, and able, to effect their own well-being.

Kate Neil: Nutrition Consultant
The Institute For Optimum Nutrition
5 Jerdan Place
London SW6 1BE
Tel: 071-385 7984

British Nutrition Foundation
15 Belgrave Square, London SW1X 8PS
Tel: 071-235 4904

The Nutri Centre is located on the lower ground floor of the Hale Clinic in 7 Park Crescent, London W1N 3HE. The prestigious (Nash Terrace) crescent is only a few minutes away from underground stations at Great Portland Street, Regents Park and Baker Street.

Clients are often faced with a dilemma when they have been prescribed or recommended a course of nutritional regime by their practitioner or Nutritionist

One often doesn't even know where to begin to find a company which provides all the products he or she needs. It may mean placing orders with a number of different manufacturers whose despatch times may vary. Consequently the institution of the regime is delayed or becomes staggered. Since delay can cause further upset to someone already in distress and staggering can mean that it takes longer for the full benefit of the treatment to be effected and felt (nutrients interact with each other and the regime will have been designed with this in mind) the client may lose heart and motivation.

In an effort to circumvent some of these problems some practitioners have arrangements with certain manufacturer's or else stock the remedies themselves. But time spent in administering the purchase and sale of remedies simply increases the stress load on practitioners and their practices.

For those individuals who do not wish to see a practitioner for any specific illness there is problem of trying to obtain professional advice on the use of vitamins and nutritional products to supplement their diet.

The aim of the recently opened NUTRI CENTRE at the Hale Clinic in London is to lift all of these burdens from practitioners and clients. Essentially it stocks or has access to the most extensive range of nutritional supplements – – from those you would find in a health food shop, to practitioner products, to exclusive lines, even to the occasional batch made up for specific requirements.

Now clients can visit or contact the Nutri Centre knowing that it can almost certainly provide all the products that have been recommended. And if, with this relative ease of availability a client begins to feel better sooner, the incentive to keep going with the regime becomes stronger and healing is achieved at a much faster rate.

Suitably qualified staff are also available to give professional advice on improving compliance of the regime to maximise its therapeutic benefits.

The Nutri Centre operates a prompt and reliable mail order service for those not fortunate enough to live or work within striking distance, and next day delivery is guaranteed. This service can also be extended to ordering "repeats" enabling them to maintain continuity of the Dietary Supplementation Therapy. The intention, therefore, is that clients from anywhere in the country should be able to order their supplies from just one phone call to the centre.

*"The Nutrition Centre's influence on the industry as a whole will be considerable,
and indeed, it is already leading the way in a number of areas..."*

Jan de Vries (June 1991)

COMPLETE RANGE OF PRACTITIONER PRODUCTS

Exclusive distributors of Scientific Consulting Services Products (USA), N.F. Products (USA), Thorne Research Products (USA) and NATREN Probiotics (USA).

Lamberts	Blackmores	Health Plus	Oligoplex
Nutri-West	Healthlink	Quest	Agnolyt
Biocare	Natures Own	Solgar	Heel
G&G	Cantassium	Lewis	Dr.Reckeweg
Natural Flow	Nature's Plus	Bio-Science	Enzyme Process
Cytoplan	Advanced Nutrition	Beres	Standard Process
Nutriscene	Healthy Body Products	Arophar	Dr Donsbach
			Jason Winter

The most comprehensive stockist of vitamin and nutritional supplements, homeopathic and biochemic remedies, herbal and Ayurvedic products and special diets

Healthcraft	Kordel	Seven Seas	Celaton
Lanes	Bioceuticals	Ortis	Floradix
Fsc	Meadowcroft	Comvita	Seatone
Power	Biohealth	Kwai	Wassen
Am Nutrition	Healthlife	Hofels	Lifeplan
Regina	Effamol	Pure-Gar	
Bioforce	Weleda	Salus-Haus	Heath & Heather
Potters	Newera	Wala	Swedish Bitters
Gerards	Khan Marigold	Arkopharma	Herbs of Grace
Bach	Ayurvedic Co.	Biostrath	Dried Herbs
Nelsons	of Great Britain	Obbekjaers	Planetary Formulas
Ainsworth			Specialist
Kan Herbals	East-West Herbs	Pascoe	Herbal Supplies

SPECIALIST PRODUCTS

Green Magma	Superdophillus	Algivit	Aloe Vera Juice
Chlorella	Primedophillus	Colon	Argille Clay
Guarana	Pfaffia	Cleansing Kits	Seavit
Imedeen	Kervrans Silica	Elagen	Viracin
Tanalbit	Blue-Green Algae	Tea-Tree Pess.	Tree Syrup

SPECIALIST SKINCARE/COSMETICS DENTAL PRODUCTS

Yin Yang	Rachael Perry	Blackmores	Annemarie Borlind
Austrian Moor	Millcreek	Tonialg	Aromatherapy Oils
Weleda	Pierre Cattier	Antica	Dead Sea Products
Tisserand	Bodytreats	Gerards	Kneipp

EXTENSIVE RANGE OF HEALTH BOOKS

LIBRARY/ BOOKSHOP/ EDUCATION CENTRE

The Centre incorporates a Library/ Bookshop with an extensive selection of books, not only on health and nutrition but also on the whole range of alternative and complementary therapies, self development and psychology, and new age. With no obligation to buy, clients are encouraged to browse-there are plenty of leaflets around advertising courses and seminars relating to lifestyle and health. The Centre is uniquely placed to make a positive contribution to education.

Books/ Information on:

Alternative Therapies: Aromatherapy & Massage, Acupuncture, Alexander Technique, Bach Flower Therapy, Crystal Therapy, Chiropractice, Homoeopathy, Iridology, Kinesiology, Osteopathy, Reflexology, Shiatshu, Spiritual Healing, Tibetan medicine.

Natural Health: Ailments, Allergies, Fitness, Slimming & Beauty, Food Combining, General Good Health, Healthy Non-vegetarian cook books, Herbs & Herbal Medicine, Macrobiotics, Natural Food Healing, Nutrition, Parents & Childcare, Special Diets, Vegetarianism, Vitamins & Minerals, Women's Health.

Environment: Green issues.

Self Development & Psychology: Positive Thinking, Recovery, Motivation & Self Improvement

New Age: General New age, Yoga & Meditation.

HOW TO FIND US

The Centre is located on the lower ground floor, being served by a lift for easy access by disabled visitors.

OPENING TIMES:
Mon - Fri   9am - 7pm
Week-end Hrs.: Please phone
for further information.

MAIL ORDER HOTLINE: 071-436 5122/ 071-631 0156
★ ALL MAJOR CREDIT CARDS ACCEPTED FOR PAYMENT
★ ORDERS PLACED BY NOON DESPATCHED SAME DAY

NUTRITIONAL THERAPY

MERSEYSIDE

H. Simpson, D.O., N.C.S.O., M.G.O.(LON.), M.I.C.A.K.,
M.R.S.H., M.H.P.A., M.A.A., M.C.K.O.R.E.   0744 88 3737

SOMERSET

Complementary Medicine Centre, 9 Corporation Street,
Taunton, Somerset TA1 4AJ   0823 325022

OSTEOPATHY

OSTEO. (bone) PATHY (feeling) originated in the
USA by A.T. Still who was dissatisfied with the
medical approach to disease.

Today's understanding of OSTEOPATHY has
been the manipulation of bones and joints. now
with scientific progress, the understanding of
OSTEOPATHY has widened to include treatment
of ORGAN DISEASE, NEUROLOGICAL AND
SKIN DISORDERS etc.

More recently, cranial manipulation has widened
the scope of OSTEOPATHY even further to
include treatment of head injuries e.g. traffic
accidents, birth trauma etc.

In the U.K. there are many colleges teaching
osteopathy – and many associations, directors
and registers of qualified osteopaths eg. (in alpha-
betical order).

MBEOA – Member of the British and European
Osteopathic Association.

MBNOA – Member of the British Naturopathic
Osteopathic Association.

MCO – Member of The College of
Osteopaths.

MCrOA – Member of The Cranial Osteopathic
Association.

MGO – Member of The Guild of Osteopaths.

MNTOS – Member of The Natural Therapeutic &
Osteopathic Society.

MRO – Member of The Register of
Osteopaths.

William H. C. Wright, B.Sc., N.D., D.O.,
M.Cr.O.A.
Hon Secretary of The Cranial Osteopathic
Association
478 Baker Street
Enfield
Middlesex EN1 3QS
Tel: 081-367 5561

British & European Osteopathic Association
6 Adele Road
Teddington, Middlesex
Tel: 081-977 8532

British College of Naturopathy and Osteopathy
Frazer House, 6 Netherall Gardens
Hampstead, London NW3 5RR
Tel: 071-435 7830 (clinic), 071-435 6464 (college)

British Osteopathic Association
8–10 Boston Place, Marylebone
London NW1 6QH
Tel: 071-262 5250

General Council & Register of Osteopaths
56 London Street
Reading
Tel: 0734 576585

Independent Register of Manipulative Therapists
32 Lodge Drive, Palmers Green
London N13 5JZ
Tel: 081-886 3120

DEVON

Betty Williams, D.O., M.G.O., M.I.A.T., M.H.P.A., M.I.C.M.
0803 843492

OSTEOPATHY

DERBYSHIRE

John Lewis,
M.Sc., D.O., Dip.Ac.(Aur)Hons., M.A., A., A.M.G.O., M.B.F.O.
Osteopathy, Acupuncture, Auriculotherapy, Remedial Massage
11 Level Lane, Buxton. Tel: 0298 25467

HAMPSHIRE

Osteopathy, Cranial Osteopathy at The Southsea
Centre for Complementary Medicine   0705 874748

LONDON

Juliette Cole, D.O., M.R.O., Registered Osteopath   071-431 6744
Violet Hill Studios   071-624 6101

The Nutri Centre, Specialists in Vitamin & Nutritional
Supplements including Practitioners Products. 7 Park Crescent,
London W1N 3HE   071-436 5122 FAX 071-436 5171

Ray Osbourne, Osteopath, N.D., D.O., M.R.O., B.Sc., The
South London Natural Health Centre   071-720 8817

Solveig Brazier-Hollins, Osteopath, N.D., M.R.N., D.O., M.R.O.,
The South London Natural Health Centre   071-720 8817

Mr. Rupert Chapman, D.O.(Hons), M.R.O.
43A Warwick Way, London SW1V 1QS
Tel: 071 834 0861

OSTEOPATHIC INFORMATION SERVICE

Osteopathy is a therapy complementary to medicine. It aims to ensure that the muscles, bones, ligaments and joints within the body are fully functional at all times. There are now over 2,000 osteopaths working all around the UK, treating over 1 million people. The Osteopathic Information Service can offer fact-sheets giving straightforward information about osteopathy and how to find an osteopath near to you.

The Osteopathic Information Service represents: the Guild of Osteopaths, the College of Osteopaths, the Natural Therapeutic and Osteopathic Society and Register, the British and European Osteopathic Association and the General Council and Register of Osteopaths.

Osteopathic Information Service
37 Soho Square, London W1V 5DG
Telephone: 071-439 7177

LOTHIAN

George Andrew, D.O., M.R.O.   031-551 5091

Alison Bleasby, B.Sc.(Hons.), M.C.O. Cranial Osteopathy and
Naturopathy   031-551 5091

MERSEYSIDE

H. Simpson, D.O.-N.C.S.O., M.G.O.(Lon.), M.I.C.A.K.,
M.R.S.H., M.H.P.A., M.A.A., M.C.K.O.R.E.   0744 88 3737

OXFORDSHIRE

Nigel C. Lane, D.O., M.R.O.   0491 579996
OR 0860 618006

SOMERSET

Complementary medicine Centre, 9 Corporation Street,
Taunton, Somerset TA1 4AJ   0823 325022
or Redgate Medical Centre, Westonsoyland, Bridgwater,
Somerset TA6 5BF   0278 444411

SURREY

Farnham Holistic Centre, Tilford Road, Farnham, Surrey
GU9 8HU   0252 734445

E. SUSSEX

R. Thurstan, D.M.O., M.Phy.A., M.B.E.O.A., The Cottage
Clinic, 25 Sea Road, Bexhill-on-Sea   0424 222070

Continuing Professional Development

OXFORD SCHOOL OF OSTEOPATHY

TWO YEAR PART TIME DIPLOMA COURSE IN OSTEOPATHY (D.O.)

The Oxford School of Osteopathy offers mature, vocationally motivated students the opportunity to achieve a formal qualification in the rapidly expanding field of osteopathy.

Graduates will be eligible to apply for Membership of The Guild of osteopaths.

Admission to courses commencing in March 93 and March 94, based at the Department of Continuing Education, Rewley House, Oxford will be restricted to:

1. **State Resgistered Nurses.**
2. **State Registered/Chartered Physiotherapists.**
3. **Students with an appropriate qualification in an aligned subject e.g. physiology, remedial massage.**

Prospective students should apply to:

The Principal, OSO, DOYLE Croft, PO Box 67, Banbury OX16 8LE
Tel: (0869) 38353

OZONE THERAPY

Ozone has a long pedigree in industry with water purification as its widest application. Medical Ozone has been used since 1959. Ozone is one of the most effective antiviral, antifungal and anti-microbial agents known to us. It is widely used in Germany and Austria, but is hardly known in the U.K. The range of conditions for which this treatment is used is wide and includes many viral conditions (acute and chronic), fungal infections, badly healing wounds or ulcers and any condition where there is a lack of oxygen in tissues such as occurs in heart disease, angina and peripheral blood vessel disease. It is also used as an adjunct in holistic cancer therapies because of its oxygenating effect and has been shown to have immune-stimulating and anti-inflammatory properties in chronic inflammatory conditions of the bowel and joints. It can be used as a treatment on its own or combined with other therapies such as chelation and nutritional therapies for heart disease and other conditions.

Dr F. Schellander
Liongate Clinic, 8 Chilston Road
Tunbridge Wells, Kent TN4 9LT
Tel: 0892 543535

Liongate Clinic

8 Chilston Road, Tunbridge Wells, Kent TN4 9LT
Telephone: 0892 543535.

A holistic private medical clinic offering CHELATION THERAPY and OZONE THERAPY for HEART DISEASE, ARTERIOSCLEROSIS and related conditions.

Also at:
Newport Clinic for Alternative Medicine, 4 Abbey Court, High Street, Newport, Shropshire TF10 7BW. Tel. 0952 813219.

PERSONAL DEVELOPMENT

Given the proliferation of specialised, New Age therapies, we have sought to facilitate a distinction between Personal and Spiritual Development activities (see 'Spiritual Development').

'Personal Development' defines, in this Guide, activities which purport to *develop to full potential* – and to, subsequently, *integrate* – the *natural processes* of Thought, Feeling and Sensation of the Social Person. As such, they are understood to embrace the *Functional* aspect of Homo Sapiens, developing under the sway of the *unconscious* will (or Spirit) of the subject, within the context of the 'social complicity'. The perceived goal is a clear-thinking, emotionally resilient and physically competent person – with an equally balanced awareness of Self, Society and the Natural world. Whilst such development clearly involves Physical well-being, Personal Development generally alludes to and focuses upon Mental Development and the integration of the Personality. As such, it is the basis for worldy excellence and the 'fertile ground' for further, Individual (Spiritual) attainments – as may be believed in, or considered possible and desirable. Deliberate, explicit development on the *Being* aspect of the subject is not usually considered in this context.

John Perrott
Research and Counselling Director
The S.E.E.D. Institute
10 Magnolia Way
Fleet, Hants GU13 9JZ
Tel/Fax: 0252 626448

PILATES

This is a physical and mental exercise system based on the principles of the Pilates (Pil-lah-tee) method of body control, balance and rehabilitation.

The technique originally designed for dancers is now suitable for everybody, regardless of age, profession and physical strength. The exercise system involves a series of slow, controlled movements designed to increase body awareness and improve posture and shape.

Its proven ability to increase the body's balance, strength and stamina have led to it being described as the complete body exercise of the nineties, that improves muscle tone evenly throughout the body. Absolutely no previous experience of bodywork is needed.

The exercises, at first learnt under close supervision, are designed to be practised with the body, mind and breath in harmony, resulting in graceful, flowing movements. The central idea of the system is to encourage the creation of a strong, firm and supple centre by working with the muscles of the stomach, hip and lower back. It increases resistance to fatigue and helps to achieve the calm state of mind necessary to cope with the stress of everyday life.

Simon Brown
Community Health Foundation
188 Old Street
London EC1V 98P
Tel: 071-251 4076

POLARITY THERAPY

Polarity Therapy is a holistic approach to health and healing, which was first developed 50 years ago by Dr. Randolph Stone of Chicago. It is a profound system which combines therapeutic touch, cleansing diet, special exercises and awareness of the effects of our thoughts and emotions.

Polarity Therapy helps the body to heal naturally because it works with the whole person. It offers a natural way of balancing physical, emotional and mental energies.

In Polarity Therapy, pain and suffering are seen to be the result of blocked energy and so Polarity practitioners are trained to understand and release these blocks and to help the client get in touch with their own core energy. When the energy flow becomes balanced, this can have a transformative effect on heatlh and well-being.

The Polarity Therapy Association
11 The Lea, Allesley Park
Coventry CV5 9HY

LONDON

Marion Jenkins, R.P.T.   081-888 6982
Violet Hill Studios   071-624 6101

Erik J. Van Vessem, R.P.T., A.S.K., 2a Thorney Crescent,
London SW11 3TR   071-223 3953

Francoise Wright, R.P.T., Dip.I.O.N., Hampstead, Streatham
City   071-435 4842

MIDDLESEX

Undo Blockages with Bodywork, Diet, Exercise and
Counselling   081-866 1148

PSYCHIC COUNSELLING

Psychic Counselling is the application of a practitioner's natural psychic abilities together with a knowledge of various forms of Healing, Psychology and Alternative Medicines.

Practitioners of Psychic Counselling are caring people who have taken a full course of instruction at The National College of Psychic Counselling. Development in various fields of psychic work, for example Clairvoyance, are an important and integral part of their training. Also of importance is instruction in Counselling Techniques and Spiritual Healing.

Psychic Counselling should not be confused with simple mediumship as it goes much further in helping a client with his or her problems.

Accredited Psychic Counsellors carry the initials, A.M.A.P.C. or R.M.A.P.C. (Associate or Registered Member of The Association of Psychic Counsellors.) after their names. Exceptional Psychic Counsellors are granted a Fellowship and carry the initials F.A.P.C. after their names.

**The National College of Psychic Counselling
181 The Downs, Harlow, Essex CM20 3RH**

The Association of Psychic Counsellors

The Association of Psychic Counsellors was formed in **1986** to provide an organisation with a membership of skilled practitioners who have attended courses of instruction in various fields of **psychic development, psychology, alternative medicine and spiritual healing** with us. As a result all members are ethical, professional and have their 'feet firmly on the ground', avoiding as much as possible, the mystical trappings associated with psychic work.

There are three grades of membership:

Associate (A.M.A.P.C.); **Registered** (R.M.A.P.C.) and the highest grade **Fellowship** (F.A.P.C.).

A list of members can be obtained by sending a Stamped Self addressed Envelope to:

**Ruby Fowles
P.O. Box 2126, Harlow
Essex CM20 3AE**

The National College of Psychic Counselling

EXCITING – STIMULATING – FASCINATING – IMPRESSIVE – INSPIRATIONAL

Have all been used in testimonials received about our Psychic Counselling Diploma Course. However, we have deliberately omitted the words **'INTOXICATING'** and **'STAGGERING'** as we would not like to give the wrong impression, but they never-the-less equally apply to what is probably the most interesting course available anywhere in this country.

Held throughout the year, our part-time Diploma Course is run over six full weekends on a monthly basis. there is no starting date and you complete the course when you have attended all six weekends. Naturally, we suggest that you start as early as possible, for the sooner you start the sooner you can complete this **UNIQUE** course and be the proud owner of the only Diploma in Psychic Counselling available in this or any other country.

Regarding the qualifications required to take the course, all we ask is that you are 21 years of age or older and that you have a sincere desire to help other people with their problems. There is no need to have been involved in psychic work before as we treat all new students as total beginners.

Examples of the subjects covered on the full course are:

**Mediumstic Development   Counselling Techniques
Various fields of Psychoogy   Numerology   Palmistry
Stress Management   Dream Interpretation   Spiritual healing
Dowsing for Allergies   Colour Healing
Alternative Medicine and much more**

Please note that all students are assessed for suitability on their first day of attendance. If you would like to know more and receive a copy of our free prospectus, give us a ring on 0279 425284 or should you prefer, you can write to us at:

The National College of Psychic Counselling, 181 The Downs, Harlow, Essex CM20 3RH

PSYCHIC COUNSELLING

MIDDLESEX

TEMPLE

Psychic Counsellor, R.M.A.P.C.,
Healing – including animals
Workshops – on Psychic awareness
On Sale – Crystals, minerals, gemstones, pendulums,
jewellery etc.
Telephone: 081-367 1495

SOMERSET

Complementary Medicine Centre, 9 Corporation Street,
Taunton, Somerset TA1 4AJ   0823 325022

SUSSEX

The Floatarium, 21 Bond Street, Brighton BN1 1RD   0273
679555 Fax: 0273 601992

British Astrological & Psychic Society

Booklet/Register of Consultants
Basic Astrological course. Meetings, etc. Send 90p stamps
**BAPS, 124 Trefoil Crescent, Broadfield,
Crawley, Sussex RH11 9EZ**

PSYCHOTHERAPY

Psychotherapy is a way of attending to a person's way of being in relation to others and the world. Usually, people seek psychotherapy at times in their lives when they find themselves in crisis or transition. They may feel stuck or confused or without purpose or meaning. Sometimes these moments of particular crisis or strain offer the opportunity to find deeper resources and under-standing within ourselves and to discover more zest for life.

A psychotherapist provides a particular context in which to explore personal issues, feelings and meanings in depth and over time. This context is characterised by a non-judgmental relationship within particular boundaries of time and space – usually fifty minutes for a session in a consistent pattern over months and years. A person may come for therapy once, twice or more times a week. Shorter-term counselling or therapy may also be available for someone to focus on very immediate problems in a more practical way.

There are a variety of forms of psychotherapy and counselling. The School of Psychotherapy and Counselling at Regents College places particular emphasis on examining the philosophical basis and assumptions in psychotherapy and is committed to an existential approach. Therapy may enable a person to explore immediate concerns in living, to identify patterns of coping that originate from childhood experience. It may also provide a dialogue in which to examine values and beliefs that shape our relationship to the demands of living and facing dying.

There are often links to be made between physical symptoms and ill-health and disturbance in our mental well-being. There are many ways and means – dreams, physical symptoms, thoughts and fantasies – through which we can come to recognise the integral nature of psyche and soma. These would all be included and attended to in the process of psycho-therapy.

Rosalind Pearman:
Core Faculty Lecturer
School of Psychotherapy and Counselling
Regent's College, Inner Circle
Regent's Park
London NW1 4NS
Tel: 071-487 7406

British Association of Psychotherapists
37 Mapesbury Road, London NW2
Tel: 081-346 1747

BUCKINGHAMSHIRE

Joyce Parsons,

R.G.N., S.C.M., D.H.P., M.N.A.H.P.
Aylesbury (0296) 24854
Specialises in treating stress-related conditions such
as anxiety, hypertension, migraine, overweight,
PMT, skin complaints and smoking.

DERBYSHIRE

Maggie Naish, Cert. in Counselling, Member B.A.C., R.G.N.,
Natural Choice Therapy Centre, 24 St. John Street, Ashbourne,
Derbyshire DE6 1GH   0335 46096

DEVON

Simon Bush, Cert. in Applied Social Studies (Bristol University)
Certificated Instructor in Constructive Living (U.S.A.). Contact The
Clinic, 37 St Peter St., Tiverton   0884 255990

Jeff Parsons, Dip.Ed.(Counselling), D.H.P., M.N.A.H.P.   0884 255990

ESSEX

Life-Force Centre for Natural Well-Being   0206 250071

PSYCHOTHERAPY

ESSEX

HAMPSHIRE

John Perrott, M.I.S.M.A., M.T.M.I., The S.E.E.D. Institute, 10 Magnolia Way, Fleet, Hants GU13 9JZ   0252 626448
See our Ad under Courses & Tuition

LANCASHIRE

The National College, 12 Cross St, Nelson, Lancs BB9 7EN
0282 699378

LONDON

Shai V. Gerhardt, Qualified Psychotherapist
071-435 1490

PSYCHOTHERAPY

SOMERSET

Complementary medicine Centre, 9 Corporation Street, Taunton, Somerset TA1 4AJ **0823 325022**
or Redgate Medical Centre, Westonsoyland, Bridgwater, Somerset TA6 5BF **0278 444411**

SURREY

Farnham Holistic Centre, Tilford Road, Farnham, Surrey GU9 8HU **0252 734445**

SUSSEX

The Floatarium, 21 Bond Street, Brighton BN1 1RD **0273 679555**
Fax: **0273 601992**

PURIFICATION

With drugs, toxic chemicals and pesticides, we live in a biochemical society, where no one is exempt from the barrage of these life-hostile elements.

L. Ron Hubbard was the first to uncover that not only drugs, but also toxins, poisons and pollutants remain lodged in the fatty tissues of the body and cause a wide variety of harmful mental and physical side-effects. They affect a person's health, attitude, learning rate and personality.

Street drugs and even medical drugs such as diet pills, codeine, novocaine and others became restimulated years after they were taken, impairing a person's abilities and dulling awareness.

To remedy this he developed the Purification® program, an exact regimen of exercise, sauna and nutritional supplements. It has successfully helped over 100,000 people and freed them from the harmful effects of toxic substances. The program is fully described in his book – *Clear Body Clear Mind: The Effective Purification Program.*

People are living healthier, drug-free and toxin-free lives as a result of his researches and writings, professionally supervised purification programs and free health consultations are available from one of the following centres around the U.K.

Hubbard Foundation (U.K.)
St. Hill Manor
East Grinstead, W. Sussex
Tel: 081-577 2877

Narconon Drug & Alcohol Rehabilitation Programme

- A truly workable road out for drug and alcohol abusers
- Comfortable drug-free withdrawal
- Uses sauna, nutritional supplements and exercise
- Has a 75% success rate of keeping people off drugs for good
- Gets the person back in control his/her life
- Methods developed by L. Ron Hubbard

CALL 0892 661562
31A High Street, East Grinstead, Sussex

BIRMINGHAM

Birmingham Purification Centre
Information Line 081-577 2877

DEVON

Plymouth Purification Centre
Information Line 081-577 2877

DORSET

Bournemouth Purification Centre
Information Line 081-577 2877

DUBLIN

Dublin Purification Centre
Information Line 081-577 2877

EDINBURGH

Edinburgh Purification Centre
Information Line 081-577 2877

LONDON

London Purification Centre
Information Line 081-577 2877

MANCHESTER

Manchester Purification Centre
Information Line 081-577 2877

EAST SUSSEX

Brighton Purification Centre
Information Line 081-577 2877

Hove Purification Centre
Information Line 081-577 2877

PURIFICATION

WEST SUSSEX

Chichester Purification Centre
Information Line   081-577 2877

East Grinstead Purification Centre
Information Line   081-577 2877

TYNE AND WEAR

Sunderland Purification Centre
Information Line   081-577 2877

RADIANCE TECHNIQUE®

The Radiance Technique® is a transcendental energy science, a meditation with the hands, an inner technique founded on a universal spirituality. The seven degrees of the authentic system were rediscovered from Tibetan Sacscrit sutras in the last century and now provide a highly effective method for relaxing, calming, revitalising and energising in our twentieth century world.

At its heart, this is a system of awakening from within, of touching the silent centre and giving and receiving transcendental energy. Benefiting every level of our body-mind-spirit dynamic, it promotes our personal development, our healing/wholing and our pursuit of our highest goals. It is a simple hands-on system, may be learned by young and old, and can easily be used on a daily basis.

You may learn TRT for yourself in a professional seminar from an accredited teacher or you may receive sessions from a Transcendental Practitioner. Many TRT teachers have a wide outreach making the technique available regionally in Britain and Europe. Our International (TRTAI) and British (TRTAGB) Associations publish books, regular journals and newsletters. Please be in touch with a teacher or Transcendental Practitioner for further information.

Ingrid St Clare
The Radiance Technique® (Seminars)
8 Furnace Lane, Finedon
Northamptonshire NN9 5NZ
Tel: 0536 725292

LONDON

The Radiance Technique –London and Regions
Ingrid St Clare
T.R.T. accredited teacher and Transcendental Practitioner
Telephone: 0536 725292

RADIESTHESIA

(see also **MEDICAL DOWSING**)

The term 'radiesthesia' is synonymous with medical dowsing and comes from the work of the French monks during the last century who used the dowsing faculty to discover the disease from which their patients were suffering and to determine the remedy which best suited the patients at that particular time. Dowsing has been widely used in the medical profession, and the Medical Society for the Study of Radiesthesia was formed in 1939. Radiesthesia is used by many practitioners in complementary medicine and courses on medical dowsing are run by the Maperton Trust. Dowsing is used to find water, minerals, faults in electrical supply systems, and even by soldiers in Vietnam to trace underground tunnels. Anyone can learn to dowse for their medicinal or nutritional supplements, and courses are run by the Member Organisations of the Confederation of Radionic and Radiesthesic organisations.

c/o The Maperton Trust
Wincanton
Somerset BA9 8EH

RADIONICS

Radionics is totally non-invasive and does not react with other forms of medication. It can be used to advantage with orthodox western and other forms of medicine.

As radionics deals with energy it can be practised at a distance and many practitioners have patients overseas.

The radionic practitioner is concerned with a patient's overall level of health and well being; a patient's named disease or symptoms are like the visible tip of an iceberg; the remaining, unseen part of the iceberg representing deeper levels of the patient's being of which he is usually unaware. Since radionics enables the practitioner to deal with the *whole* 'iceberg' – that is to say the *whole* patient – he concerns himself with the complete person rather than just the symptoms.

The initial training of radionic practitioners lasts for three to four years, during which the practitioner learns to make an analysis of the health of the patient by taking readings of the physical, emotional, mental, and in some cases in the spiritual aspects. The practitioner also measures the flow of energy, takes readings of the progression towards certain major diseases, and seeks to establish the causes for any disharmony found. The practitioner, using his instruments, then provides the energy to bring the patient back to a balanced state of health.

THE HISTORY OF RADIONICS
The principles of radionics were first discovered by a distinguished American physician, Dr. Albert Abrams, A.M., L.L.D., M.D. Born in San Francisco in 1863, Dr. Abrams took his medical degree at Heidelberg, graduating with first class honours and the Gold Medal of the University. He went on to become one of America's leading specialists in diseases of the nervous system, a respected teacher and writer of medical textbooks.

Further information on treatment, training, organisations, books etc., can be obtained from:

The Confederation of Radionic & Radiesthesic Organisations
c/o The Maperton Trust
Somerset BA9 8EH
Tel: 0963 32651

REBIRTHING

Rebirthing is a safe, simple, yet deeply profound process of learning to 'allow' our unique consciously connected breath, to access moments of experience that have lead us to make the misguided choice of withdrawing life, rather than integrating the valuable lessons offered.

In a typical session lasting 2–4 hours you will be instructed, whilst lying on your back, to focus on relaxing into your body and a connected breathing pattern. As you maintain this connection, you will become sufficiently energised with breath and probably experience currents of energy playing throughout your body. These currents tend to activate sub-conscious material which may be experienced in terms of feelings, thoughts, emotions, memories, dreams, fantasies or simply unfamiliar sensations. It is not uncommon for the person experiencing these phenomena to fight, control, direct, avoid or even totally deny them. It is, however, the total 'allowing' that quickly leads through the process into an extremely pleasant state of holistic awareness that many have described as "bliss". It is the light at the end of the journey which heralds that whatever material during this session was activated by the breath, has now been integrated rather than suppressed.

It is this learning to 'allow' whilst connectedly breathing in a relaxed manner that is the real art of Rebirthing.

Clive Musson-Chabrier, M.G.P.P.R.
Guild of Professional Practising Rebirthers
Tel: 071-229 4672

British Rebirth Society
18 Woodfield Road, Redland, Brisjtol BS6 6JQ

REFLEXOLOGY

Reflexology treatment involves massage to reflex points in the feet to treat different disorders in the body.

There are areas in the feet which relate to all the parts of the body with the right foot relating to the right side of the body and the left foot to the left side. A precise form of massage is given to the reflex areas, using mainly the thumbs and to a lesser extent the fingers, to balance the energy flow to the corresponding area of the body. The method is based on a system of longitudinal zones in the body which were first described by a Dr. Fitzgerald in the early 1900's.

As the various reflex points are worked on, different sensations will be experienced by the patient, the more tender a reflex area is, the more out of balance the corresponding part of the body. The treatment should not, however, be very uncomfortable since the pressure used is adjusted to suit the patient.

There are certain conditions where treatment is not suitable or where extra care is required when giving treatment but in general the method can be used to help a wide range of disorders. An additional advantage of the treatment is that it is extremely relaxing.

Nicola Hall, Chairman
The British Reflexology Association
Monks Orchard, Whitbourne
Worcester WR6 5RB
Tel: 0886 21207

AVON

REFLEXOLOGY

BERKSHIRE

Rosemary School of Natural Therapy, 10 Pine Ridge, Newbury, Berkshire RG13 2NQ **0635 31679**

Mrs Naomi Shepherd, M.A.R., I.T.E.C.
Penfold, Lodge Road, Hurst, Reading, RG10 0EG. Tel 0734 340755 *also at* Natural Therapy Clinic, 2 Boyne Valley Road, Maidenhead, Berks. SL6 4ED. Tel 0628 72005

CUMBRIA

Salon Elysée Hair & Beauty,
Comprehensive range of treatments available in relaxing surroundings to reduce stress and revitalise energy.
Reflexologist: **Elizabeth A. Weir,** M.B.R.A., M.I.F.A.
Tel: 0228 28222

DERBYSHIRE

Alison Mold, B.Ed.(Hons), Dip.B.W.Y. (Cert. in Remedial Yoga), Dip.S.P.A., I.S.P.A., Natural Choice, 24 St. John Street, Ashbourne, Derbyshire DE6 1GH **0335 46096**

Mary Smallwood, M.B.R.A., S.C.M., S.R.N., Natural Choice, 24 St. John Street, Ashbourne, Derbyshire DE6 1GH **0335 46096**

ESSEX

Lorraine Myers, M.A.R., Reflexologist
Rainbow Cottage, The Street, Chappel, Colchester, Essex CO6 2DD
Please call me to discuss how Reflexology can dissolve tension/ stress, allowing the body/mind to heal specific problems. Clinic at Chappel. Home visits available.
Telephone 0787 224429

Pam Alcock, M.B.R.A. **0206 271331** OR **0206 561150**

Pauline Shorey, Dip.A.P.M., I.T.E.C., A.I.P.T.I., Association Complimentary Health, Sandleigh Road, Leigh **0702 714862**

Great Clacton Natural Healing Centre, 6 St. John's Road, Great Clacton, Essex **0255 436059**

Susan Ager, R.M.A.N.M., Reflexology for Stress and Stress Related Disorders, Migraine, Asthma and much more **0245 74010**

Life-Force Centre for Natural Well-being **0206 250071**

GLOUCESTERSHIRE

Valerie Johnston, D.E.A.S., I.T.E.C., L.T.Phys., M.I.P.T.I., offers a psycho-spiritual approach **0242 224283**

HAMPSHIRE

Alison Perrott, S.P.Dip.A., M.I.S.P.A., M.I.S.M.A., M.A.S.K., M.T.M.I., The S.E.E.D. Institute, 10 Magnolia Way, Fleet, Hants GU13 9JZ **0252-626448**
See our Ad under Courses & Tuition

HERTFORDSHIRE

Su Hagan, S.P.Dip.A., M.I.S.P.A., M.T.M.I., The S.E.E.D. Institute, Stable Flat, Serge Hill Road, Bedmond, Abbots Langley, Herts WD5 0RY **0923-268898**
See our Ad under Courses & Tuition

Margaret Izod, M.D.M.A., Reflexology, Homoeopathy, Bach Flower, Acupuncture, 44a High Street, Hoddesdon, Herts EN11 8DA **0992 443462** OR **0279 651063**

KENT

Jane Higgs, M.A.R., I.T.E.C.
Reflexologist & Aromatherapist
1 Shurland Avenue, Sittingbourne, Kent
Telephone 0795 424821

LONDON

Mark Mordin, M.B.R.A., M.R.S.S.
The Milton Natural Health Centre,
33 Milton Avenue, Highgate, London N6
Telephone: 081-340 7062

Carole Sher, Reflexology Therapist, B.A., L.L.S.A., L.C.S.P., The South London Natural Health Centre **071-720 8817**

REFLEXOLOGY

LONDON

Barbara Stanhope-Williamson, M.A.R.
(British Register of Complementary Practitioners (Reflexology))
Practices at Natureworks, W1 (opposite Selfridge's Clock)
and West Hampstead NW6
Telephone 071-625 6925

GREATER MANCHESTER

MANCHESTER SCHOOL OF MASSAGE

Diploma Courses in Massage, Aromatherapy, Reflexology, Sports therapy, on-site massage and Shiatsu. Weekday or Weekend Classes. Also Workshops available in Crystal Healing, Polarity, Bach Flower Etc. Contact: Manchester School of Massage, Freepost, Manchester M16 8HB or Telephone 061-862 9752 (Treatments also available)

MIDDLESEX

Grace Stannard, M.A.R.
9 The Crescent, Shaftesbury Avenue,
South Harrow HA2 0PJ
Telephone: 081-864 7684

SOMERSET

June Markham, S.P.Dip.A., M.I.S.P.A., The S.E.E.D. Institute,
93A Ilchester Road, Yeovil, Somerset BA21 3BJ **0935 74379**
See our Ad under Courses & Tuition

Complementary Medicine Centre, 9 Corporation Street,
Taunton, Somerset TA1 4AJ **0823 325022**

STAFFORDSHIRE

Linda J. Skellam, M.C.S.P. (S.R.P.), Leek Natural Therapy
Centre **0538 383726**

SUFFOLK

Mrs Margaret Weeds, M.I.F.A., M.B.S.R., S.P.A.Dip.M.I.P.,
T.I., I.T.E.C. 17 Freckenham Road, Worlington, Nr Mildenhall,
Suffolk IP28 8SQ **0638 716759**

SURREY

Farnham Holistic Centre, Tilford Road, Farnham, Surrey
GU9 8HU **0252 734445**

SUSSEX

The Floatarium, 21 Bond Street, Brighton BN1 1RD **0273 679555**
Fax: **0273 601 992**

YORKSHIRE

For sports injuries, back, neck and arms, leg, joint and muscle pains. Better health for mind and body. Contact:

Enrico Dodson, L.C.S.P.(Assoc.), M.I.I.R., M.B.S.A.M.
21 Cowlersley Lane, Huddersfield HD4 5TY
Telephone: 0484 641982

NORTH YORKSHIRE

REFLEXOLOGY

The whole body treatment carried out on the feet by massage. Home visits carried out in Harrogate, Wetherby and York.
For further information and appointments ring
Ian Sawkins, M.A.R. on York **0904 651544** or **422149**
York Reflexology Centre,
22A Fishergate, York YO1 4AB

WEST YORKSHIRE

REFLEXOLOGY

Reflexology an ancient healing art working on the feet to release the body's own healing powers. See courses.
June A. Jackson, M.I.I.R., M.A.R., C.M.H.
Hypnotherapist Acupuncturist.
40 Stratton Road, Brighouse HD6 3TA 0484 719343

REGRESSION

We are extraordinary beings, yet how restricted out lives can seem at times, held within the narrow confines of our sense of self limitations and belief systems! Change comes when we can step back and consider the greater perspective. Regression is a safe and loving way to do that.

So much seems to have been written about the subject and yet its potential worth is only beginning to be acknowledged. Regression is not just a process through which one catches glimpses of past lives, it is an expansion of your consciousness. In a comfortably relaxed state, normally the result of creative visualisation, we are given an opportunity to "step out of present time" into a "safe space". From that place of trust, we can observe and release the attachments and blocks that have acted like magnets to pull us repeatedly into the same situations, reactions and behaviour patterns, possibly lifetime after lifetime, narrowing our focus onto an illusion of truth about ourselves and our reality that is a scant echo of our true potential.

The release of those seeming limitations makes space for our creative spontaneity to come to the surface and flourish, to allow infinite ways of being to come into our lives, naturally.

Kathryn Player
The Sound Foundation
Robinson, Barber and Co
Connop House, 517 Hertford Road
Enfield, Middlesex EN3 5UA
Tel: 071-236 6268 or 071-582 4061
(11am–4.30pm Mon–Fri)

REGRESSION THERAPY

REIKI

DORSET

KARMIC COUNSELLING
Past-Life Readings, Regression, Acupuncture,
'Natural' Menopause Remedies, Chinese Herbal Medicine
SAE: Judy Hall, Gardens House,
Wimborne St. Giles, Dorset BH21 5NB

LONDON

PAST LIFE REGRESSION
Release restrictions from the past held in your
subconscious mind. Become free. Achieve your goals.
Gentle and healing.

ANNA MITCHEL. Tel: 071 603 5157 (W14)

SURREY

Barry McManus, B.Sc., R.N.H.P.Dip., A.P.N.T., M.I.F.A.,
10 Benhilton Gardens, Sutton, Surrey   081-641 4525

Morris Berg,
B.Ac.(Hons), Dip.T.H.P., M.N.A.C.H.P., M.A.P.R.T.
Past Life Therapy/Healing, childhood regression, releasing
trauma/abuse, shamanic therapy, general hypnotherapy/
psychotherapy. From April 1993:
Godalming 0483 416421

Past Life Regression, Aromatherapy–Reflexion
Cristina Weiland, M.A.R., A.H.A.F.
Sun Cottage, 69 Terrace Road,
Walton-on-Thames, Surrey KT12 2SW
Tel: 0932 247887

SUSSEX

The Floatarium, 21 Bond Street, Brighton BN1 1RD   0273 679555
Fax: 0273 601 992

PAST LIFE RECALL ....
. . . takes you gently into an altered state of consciousness where you can
release patterns of trauma, physical symptoms, problems in relationships,
emotional blockages and negative programming.
Mrs. E. Marsh,
Omahu, Primrose Lane, Forest Row, East Sussex RH18 5LT or
Tel: 034 282 4163
See my articles in Global Link Up, Jan 92 and Light – Spring 1992.

REIKI, pronounced ray key, is a safe, gentle and
powerful way you can help yourself and others to
relax, cope more easily with life's difficulties,
improve physical and mental health, develop your
natural healing, intuitive and creative powers, and
experience more love, joy and inner peace.

The word reiki is Japanese and comes from 'rei'
meaning cosmic, divine, and 'ki' meaning life
force. Reiki is the universal energy which creates,
nurtures, sustains all life. REIKI also describes the
natural method of healing using this energy which
Dr Mikao Usui was taught in a vision after years of
searching for the secret of healing in Christian,
Hindu and Buddhist writings. Healing means restoring harmony to mind, body, spirit.

Besides receiving the gift of healing himself, Usui
learnt how to activate it in others. This ability has
been passed down to Reikimasters. Anyone,
including children, can be 'tuned in', normally
during a 2-day workshop, and can then, using
simple touch, give Reiki treatments to themselves,
others, animals, and plants. No special gift or
knowledge is necessary. Distance healing can be
learned in a second-level workshop.

Reiki is effective alone and can be beneficially
used with other complementary and orthodox
medical treatments.

Margaret Pauffley
Reikimaster
27 Lavington Road, Ealing W13 9NN
Tel: 081-579 3813

ESSEX

Life-Force Centre for National Well-Being   0206 250071

LONDON

REIKI
Workshops, Introductory evenings, treatments
Willing to teach anywhere
Free tuition for organiser of workshop
Reikimaster Margaret Pauffley
Telephone: 081 579 3813

PRATIBHA
Osho Neo-Reiki Master
Initiations in Reiki I + II
Individual sessions and practice classes
TEL: 071-582 1794

REIKI

THE ASSOCIATION OF EUROPEAN REIKI PRACTITIONERS

AERP was set up in 1991, primarily in response to the proposed EC guidelines on Complementary Medicine. We provide a system of accreditation and insurance for those who wish to practise Reiki professionally.

A natural consequence of setting up the association has been to provide a networking system for everyone who has Reiki, and to increase public awareness of Reiki as a method of healing through attendance at exhibitions, and through the press, radio and TV.

As an association we provide a national register of practitioners and Masters, and a quarterly magazine to facilitate the sharing of experiences, and to provide a platform of exchange of information.

There are various levels of membership and membership fees; Associate membership provides anyone who has Reiki with an opportunity to connect with the wider Reiki family, Probationer membership is for those who are undertaking the necessary additional training to comply with the EC guidelines, and Full membership is for those who have received accreditation from the association. All members are eligible to vote at the AGM.

Chris Williams, Chairperson
If you would like more information, please contact:
Kate Finlayson, Administrator
8 Ashmore Road, Cotteridge
Birmingham B30 2HA

Association of European Reiki Practitioners, The Administrator, 8 Ashmoor Road, Cotteridge, Kings Norton, Birmingham B30 2HA

REIKI is an ancient art of healing by touch – REI meaning Universal, and KI meaning Life Energy. It is the life force energy that flows through everything. Reiki is a way of channelling this energy, through our hands, enabling the body to accelerate its own healing process. It not only addresses the physical disorders of the body, but also opens the mind to the causes of "dis-ease" and pain. It reinforces a person's ability to take responsibility for their life through positive change in attitudes which in turn leads to a happier and healthier life.

For information about treatment and classes contact:
Loretta Venus & Chris Williams
5 Heath Ridge, Long Ashton, Bristol BS18 9EW. Tel: 0275 394486 or

- Pam Steele, Wareham 0929-556714
- Jill Carlisle, Canterbury 0227-452070
- Fiona Gavin-Edwards, Herefordshire 0544-230973
- Roger Sapsford, London 081-769 5997
- Christine Lunt, Bristol & Manchester 0272-246581
- Janine`de Mofnay, Leeds 0532-677183
- Alice Pitt, Taunton 0823-660492
- Gilly Weaver, Weymouth 0305-832387
- Karen Cook, Stroud 0453-750088

ROLFING

Rolfing is a method of structural integration and alignment of the body developed by American biochemist Ida Rolf (1896–1979) who saw that the body's posture and muscular tensions were held in place by the sinewy web of connective tissue. These take their shape in response to injuries and traumas we have suffered, habits we have adopted and the ever present force of gravity.

The Rolfing practitioner works deeply and gently with the hands untangling the web of connective tissue. The client assists by making slow precise movement, stretching and opening the tissue. Sometimes this can be momentarily uncomfortable; for others, deep emotional release can occur during the session. The Rolfer and client work together to build the trust necessary to sustain these changes. Gradually over a series of ten sessions, posture improves, muscles reset their tone, and the body acquires a lightness and responsiveness in carriage and movement.

Improving the posture can help combat chronic fatigue, joint, muscle and back pain and aid the function of the internal organs. Rolfing is also useful in resolving unfinished emotional issues which are dramatised in the postural attitudes and chronic holding patterns of the body.

All certified Rolfers are trained by the Rolf Institute, Boulder, Colorado, U.S.A.

Ms Jennie Crewdson: Certified Rolfer
London SW1V 2DR
Tel: 071-834 1493

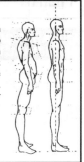
RUBENFELD SYNERGY METHOD

The Rubenfeld Synergy method is a means of contacting, expressing and working through body tensions and stored emotions by using touch, subtle movements and the verbal integration of Gestalt Therapy. A dynamic integration of body, mind and emotions.

Rubenfeld has a degree in conducting, and played the viola, piano, and oboe, Backaches and tension led her to Alexander Technique, in which she trained. Emotional release during lessons led her to Gestalt therapy and Fritz Perls. Then she met and studied with Moshe Feldenkrais.

'Synergy' has been defined as the behaviour of whole systems unpredicted by the behaviour of the individual parts. A meeting with the originator of this definition and populariser of the concept of Synergy, R. Buckminster Fuller, led to the naming of Rubenfeld's work in this way.

Rubenfeld subtly, non-intrusively and intuitively collaborates with clients to produce unexpected results, and uses the term 'experiment' to distinguish her lessons in awareness from the thoughtless repetitiveness of exercise. Based in New York, she brings a refreshing humour to her teaching.

The Institute of Structural Bodywork
c/o Roger Golten
Synergy Centre
1 Cadogan Gardens
London SW3 2RJ

SHAMANISM

The term *shaman* or *saman* comes from the language of the Tungus reindeer herders of the Lake Baikal region of Russia. Anthropologists researching and writing about indigenous healing practices the world over, have applied this term to tribal healers. The origins of shamanism pre-date recorded civilisation. Evidence of shamanic practices exists from the paleolithic period, tens of thousands of years ago, and it is the oldest way humanity sought connection with the realm of the Gods. Its practice is shared by indigenous peoples all over the world with an underlying cosmology that cuts across cultural boundaries. Today shamanism survives on all inhabited continents in less 'developed' regions in spite of the relentless onslaught of western rationalism and male dominated religion.

The shamanic view of the structure of the Universe is that of three interconnecting worlds: an underworld of 'power animals' or instinctive forces, a subterranean world of the unconscious; a sky world of guides, gods and goddesses, a rarified world of the super-conscious. Perched precariously in the middle, is the world of everyday life. To the shaman, all things are alive and interconnected in a web of beingness in which everything affects everything else. The shaman is the restorer of balance, the healer – maker of wholeness or 'holy' person – and can be thought of as the ecologist of the psyche.

Leo Rutherford, MA in holistic psychology, is the founder of Eagle's Wing Centre for contemporary shamanism and has studied with many gifted shamans and medicine people in North and South America over the last twelve years. He runs courses on many aspects of shamanism from one day to one year in duration.

Leo Rutherford
Eagle's Wing
Centre for Contemporary Shamanism
58 Westbere Road, London NW2 3RU
Tel: 071-435 8174

SHIATSU

WHAT IS SHIATSU?

Shiatsu is a Japanese word which literally translated means 'finger pressure'. However, its techniques involve not only the use of fingers, but also thumbs, palms, knees, forearms, elbows, and feet. Moreover, since it is given on the floor rather than on a couch, it gives considerable attention to the correct use of body positioning and gravity to deliver its wide range of techniques.

The full potential of Shiatsu is only realised after certain qualities have been developed within the giver. These qualities are:

● The ability to remain relaxed and comfortable irrespective of which techniques are used.
● The ability to detect subtle changes in a person's vitality through touch.
● The ability to assess a person's level of health or disease through sensitivity and the understanding of Oriental Medicine.

Shiatsu can therefore be classified as a physical therapy applied at floor level with minimum physical effort by the therapist, and which uses Oriental Medicine as its theoretical framework.

Shiatsu generally takes 2–3 years of committed study and practice to reach a professional standard of competence. However, beyond its role in the healing of others, Shiatsu is also a tremendous method of self-development. It has the effect of focusing the mind and grounding both body and mind. For this reason it heals, strengthens and develops both the giver and the recipient.

Chris Jarmey
Principal – European Shiatsu School
Central Administration
High Banks
Lockeridge, Nr Marlborough
Wiltshire SN8 4EQ
Tel: 0672 86362

SHIATSU

SHIATSU ON THE SPOT

Japanese on site massage was started in the United States in 1984 by David Palmer at Apple Computers in Silicone Valley. He then designed the folding portable massage chair which went on the market in 1986. The number of practitioners in the US was by then over 5,000. In 1989 Steve Bird, a Brighton massage therapist, introduced the first chair to the UK. Manufacture was started in late 1990 by New Concept of Tattingstone.

The type of massage given is a type of shiatsu but in the form of a Kata. This is a self contained highly studied and very effective series of movements designed specifically as a tune up for those working in high pressure situations to relax muscles, increase circulation and revitalise the receiver.

Firms already using on-site massage for their employees include, H. J. Heinz in Pittsburgh, Lockeed in Texas, Virgin Airlines, The State Department Washington, Saatchi and Saatchi London, Gold Greenlees Trott, Ad agencies BMP and DDB Needham.

Michael Hardy, M.R.S.S.
Shiatsu Acupressure Therapy
8 The Close
Tattingstone
Ipswich IP9 2PD
Tel: 0473 328705

Shiatsu Society
14 Oakdene Road, Redhill, Surrey RH1 6BT
Tel: 0737 767896

AVON

The school offers a complete range of courses from introductory classes to 3 year professional practitioner training and post-graduate courses.

For an application form and prospectus, please send 2 first class stamps to:

Bristol School of Shiatsu & Oriental Medicine, 18 Lilymead Avenue, Knowle, Bristol B54 2BX
Tel: (0272) 772809

BEDFORDSHIRE

The British School of Shiatsu-Do
(Bedford Branch)
is currently teaching Foundation Level courses.
For further information contact:
S. Wale
Telephone: 0767 40236

Sarah Wale, B.Sc.(Hons), M.R.S.S.
Registered Shiatsu Practitioner.
Wisteria House, Blunham, Bedfordshire
Tel: Biggleswade 0767 40236

DERBYSHIRE

Mike Craske, B.Sc., D.I.C., Ph.D., Dip. in Shiatsu and oriental medicine, Natural Choice Therapy Centre, 24 St. John Street, Ashbourne, Derbyshire DE6 1GH   0335 46096

DEVON

The Devon School of Shiatsu

- Regular Introductory Classes
- 1 Year Foundation Course
- 3 Year Practitioner Training Course
- Practice and Clinic Days
- In own rooms in Devonshire countryside

Full programme from:
The Devon School of Shiatsu
The Coach House, Buckyette Farm
Littlehempston, Totnes, Devon TQ9 6ND
Tel: 0803 762593

ESSEX

Great Clacton Natural Healing Centre, 6 St. John's Road, Great Clacton, Essex   0255 436059

HAMPSHIRE

The British School of Shiatsu-Do (Alton)
The Courtyard, Farringdon, Alton, Hampshire GU34 3DH
Susie Woodd, M.R.S.S.
Telephone 0420 58210
Introductory Days/Foundation Courses/Treatments

KENT

Ken Oliver, M.R.S.S.
Clinics in Maidstone, Rochester, Gravesend & Bromley
For details:
Tel: (Day) 0622 750605 (Evenings/Weekend) 0622 820397

SHIATSU

SHIATSU MASSAGE

Touching has long been established as a great way to relax. Its therapeutic value was recognised more than 5,000 years ago when Shiatsu (Shee-at-soo) massage originated. Anyone who has experienced the comforting touch of a sympathetic friend will know what a healing experience touch can be.

This simple art has developed into a powerful therapy. Shiatsu is now very popular, for example, the Community Health Foundation provides more than 3,000 Shiatsu treatments each year. Shiatsu is especially helpful for stress and stress-related symptoms.

A typical treatment lasts an hour and the patient wears loose cotton clothing. A shiatsu is a great way to find out more about your health and the condition of your body. Most people notice that after a shiatsu they feel wonderfully relaxed, and yet full of energy.

Fortunately shiatsu massage is very easy to learn. In an introductory course anyone can learn to give a full-body shiatsu to friends and family. Once learnt it is also simple to teach someone to give you a relaxing shiatsu.

Traditionally in China and Japan people working together, friends and family members regularly gave each other shiatsu to ease away aches and pains, and prevent the onset of illness.

Many people have found it is a wonderful way to enhance relationships and get to know each other. It can even be the start of an exciting new career as most introductory courses form the beginning of a three year training in Shiatsu.

Simon Brown
Community Health Foundation
188 Old Street
London EC1V 98P
Tel: 071-251 4076

SHIATSU

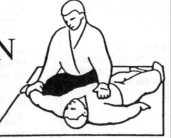

SHIATSU

The Community Health Foundation

runs a 36 hours beginner's course where you will learn
how to give a full **Shiatsu** massage and more.
Shiatsu treatments by appointment Monday–Saturday
Cost £195   Call for details **071-251 4076**

Mark Mordin, M.B.R.A., M.R.S.S.
The Milton Natural Health Centre
33 Milton Avenue, Highgate, London N6
Telephone 081-340 7062

| Fionnuala O'Hare, M.R.S.S. | 071-328 5399 |
| Violet Hill Studios | 071-624 6101 |

| Madeline Pym, M.R.S.S. | 081-802 9021 |
| Violet Hill Studios | 071-624 6101 |

Josephine Pridmore, M.R.S.S.
Shiatsu relaxes the body and mind, then a natural
healing process occurs.
Crouch End, London N8 8RH
Telephone: 081-340 0727
Also available in Bournemouth and Blandford Forum, Dorset.

Professional training in
Shiatsu,
Oriental Medicine,
Self-development
& Healing
with
The Shiatsu College
2 and 3 Year programmes at our new venue in LONDON W10

NEXT INTRODUCTORY WEEKENDS
- 3–4 APRIL 1993
- 5–6 JUNE 1993
- 31 JULY/1 AUG 1993
£58.75 inc. per weekend

*For our new 1992/3 Prospectus & booking information
please send 4 × 1st CLASS STAMPS to:*

SHIATSU COLLEGE ADMINISTRATION *(Dept ACHD).*
20A LOWER GOAT LANE, NORWICH NR2 1EL
or Telephone 0603 632555

Jon Sandifer, M.R.S.S.
Shiatsu, Macrobiotic Dietary Advice
1. Woodbridge Complementary Health Centre
   0394 388234
2. Lotus Healing Centre   **0728 723 478**
3. East West Centre   **071-251 4076**

John Tidder, M.R.S.S.,
Shiatsu Practitioner
Registered with The Shiatsu Society

114 Glebe Road, Norwich NR2 3JQ
For appointments Tel: 0603 626153

Complementary Medicine Centre, 9 Corporation Street,
Taunton, Somerset TA1 4AJ   **0823 325022**

Michael Hardy, M.R.S.S., Shiatsu and on site service, Ipswich
0473 328705

The London College of Shiatsu, 'Glanafon', 2 Sandy Lane,
Waldringfield, Nr Woodbridge, Suffolk IP12 4QY   **047336 534**

SHIATSU. One year Foundation Course begins
September. Small group ensures personal tuition
during 12 weekends in Suffolk countryside.
Neil Gulliver. Tel: Ipswich 0473 328 061

Farnham Holistic Centre, Tilford Road, Farnham, Surrey
GU9 8HU   **0252 734445**

Mrs. Susie Woodd, M.R.S.S.
Farnham Holistic Centre,
Tilford Road, Farnham, Surrey GU9 8HU
Tel: 0252 734445

The Floatarium, 21 Bond Street, Brighton BN1 1RD   **0273 679555**
Fax: 0273 601992

**INTRO EVENINGS &
BEGINNERS COURSES
IN
C R O Y D O N**
Contact: **The Enso School of Shiatsu,**
15 Crebor St, London SE22 0HF
Tel: 081 299 2152

SPIRITUAL DEVELOPMENT

Given the proliferation of specialised, New Age activities, we have sought to facilitate a distinction between Spiritual and Personal Development activities (see 'Personal Development').

Spiritual Development defines, in this Guide, activities which promote the development and integration of non-Naturally endowed, *conscious* perceptions of Thought, Feeling and Sensation and their dominion over the Natural Processes of the Social Person. As such, they are understood to develop the *Being* aspect of Homo Sapiens, demanding the participation of the *conscious will* of the subject, within the context of 'Spiritual Reality'. The intuited goal is the progressive Realisation of the Individual in a context of *transformation* and *centering* in Being – rather than Function – with a balanced awareness of Self, the Phenomenal World and Spiritual Reality. Whilst such development is clearly founded upon prior, Personal well-being, Spiritual Development addresses and focuses upon the manipulation of natural, personal resources towards the aim of manifesting the Spiritual Essence in and through Corporeality. Therefore, ongoing mental confusions and neuroses, in general, effectively block Spiritual Development.

John Perrott
Research and Counselling Director
Tel/Fax: 0252 626448
The *S.E.E.D.* Institute
10 Magnolia Way
Fleet, Hants GU13 9JZ

SPIRITUAL HEALING

Spiritual healing seeks the restoration of health at all levels of man's being irrespective of where ill-health has manifested. By the laying on of hands and by attunement through meditation, a healer seeks to induce a beneficial effect upon a patient's life force at all levels of existence. The word 'spiritual' refers to the acknowledged divine source of healing energies and to that responsive element in Man seen by healers as comprised of body, mind and spirit.

Healing may be given for any illness, stress or injury as a therapy which has no side-effects and is complementary to all others. Case histories range from the trivial to the diagnosis of terminal illness in which recovery has taken place but no-one can say in advance whether spiritual healing will be beneficial in any particular case but it happens too often to be coincidental every time. Apart from its therapeutic effect in relieving pain and in the restoration of function, spiritual healing is notable for marked improvements in patients' attitudes and their quality of life.

Spiritual healing is officially listed as a recognised therapy with the NHS. Doctors are permitted by the General Medical Council to refer their patients for healing and NFSH healers may attend hospital in-patients who request their services.

National Federation of Spiritual Healers
Old Manor Farm Studio
Church Street, Sunbury-on-Thames
Middlesex TW16 6RG
Tel: 0932 783164/5

Great Clacton Natural Healing Centre, 6 St. John's Road, Great Clacton, Essex   0255 436059

WALES

STRESS MANAGEMENT

STRESS may be good, bad, or ugly. Managing stress means learning more about what stress is, how it affects us and then learning one or more of a variety of skills which enable us to make the most of good stress, keep bad stress under control and to avoid, or to recover from, the effects of ugly stress.

We can learn to have more control over our own "inner space", both in mind and body. The result is that we maintain a good state of health, well-being and performance by our own efforts.

Stress is not a disease and stress management is not a form of therapy. The skills can be used to enhance the effectiveness of any therapy, as well as for personal and organisational development.

For further information please write to:
International Stress Management Association (U.K. Branch)
25 Sutherland Avenue
Leeds LS8 1BY

Stress Management – A Practical Introduction to Meditation – a natural approach to stress management, Tape Cassette and Booklet – VG Productions   081-341 3556
See Courses/Workshops

HAMPSHIRE

Alison Perrott, S.P.Dip.A., M.I.S.P.A., M.I.S.M.A., M.A.S.K., M.T.M.I., The S.E.E.D. Institute, 10 Magnolia Way, Fleet, Hants GU13 9JZ   Tel/Fax: 0252-626448
See our Ad under Courses & Tuition

John Perrott, M.I.S.P.A., M.T.M.I., The S.E.E.D. Institute, 10 Magnolia Way, Fleet, Hants GU13 9JZ   Tel/Fax: 0252-626448
See our Ad under Courses & Tuition

HERTFORDSHIRE

Su Hagan, S.P.Dip.A., M.I.S.P.A., M.T.M.I., The S.E.E.D. Institute, Stable Flat, Serge Hill Road, Bedmond, Abbots Langley, Herts WD5 0RY   0923-268898
See our Ad under Courses & Tuition

LOTHIAN

Terry Gower, B.Sc., Dip.Ed., N.L.P., C.M.H., C.Hyp., Hypnotherapy, Stress care counselling   031-551 5091

MIDDLESEX

Individual and Small Groups, Relaxation, Breathing, Energy Balancing   081-866 1148

SURREY

Farnham Holistic Centre, Tilford Road, Farnham, Surrey GU9 8HU   0252 734445

SUSSEX

The Floatarium, 21 Bond Street, Brighton BN1 1RD   0273 679555
Fax: 0273 601 992

TAI CHI

This ancient Chinese martial art consists of a series of slow graceful movements. Although Tai Chi can eventually be used for self defence most people practice Tai Chi to improve their physical health and for mental relaxation. It is often described as meditation in movement.

The Tai Chi movements were developed to enhance the movement of Chi energy throughout the body. Chi is a subtle form of electromagnetic energy that circulates in the same way as blood. The feeling of Chi moving well is when every cell in the body feels alive and tingling with energy.

Practitioners of Tai Chi discover peace of mind, an increase in energy with greater relaxation. More immediate benefits are better co-ordination, a feeling of being balanced and greater awareness of body and mind.

Typical Tai Chi courses begin with the short form of 64 movements progressing to the long form of more than 128 movements. Classes will often include 'sticking' and 'pushing hands' where students work in pairs to share energy, discover each other's strengths and weaknesses and learn how to let go and relax.

Simon Brown
Community Health Foundation
188 Old Street, London EC1V 98P
Tel: 071-251 4076

T'AI CHI

Teach Yourself T'ai Chi – 90 minute video, book, tape
cassette – VG Productions   **081-341 3556**
See Courses/Workshops

DEVON

LONDON

The Community Health Foundation
runs beginner's, intermediate and advanced
classes in the yang style short form and long form Tai Chi.
Call 071-251 4076 for details

School of T'ai-Chi Ch'uan,
Centre for Healing
Long Yang Form, Chi-kung, philosophy, symbolism.
Beginners Classes September, February, April.
Residential Weekends.
S.A.E. 5 Tavistock Place, London WC1H 9SS
or Tel: 081 444 6445

TRADITIONAL ORIENTAL DIAGNOSIS

Traditionally Oriental Diagnosis began in China before 3600 BC. The physicians of the period built their reputations on their ability to prevent illness through developing highly skilled, non-invasive techniques to predict tendencies towards a particular illness in the future. The patient could then make the appropriate changes in their diet and lifestyle to try and prevent that illness and improve their existing health.

Today, even with a basic understanding this becomes a powerful tool to discover your strengths and weaknesses, as well as what would increase or reduce your vulnerability to certain illnesses.

The philosophy of yin and yang is the basis of Oriental Diagnosis. If someone is more yin they would typically be more relaxed, calm, sensitive, creative, imaginative and good at dealing with wider issues whereas someone who is more yang would typically be more active, alert, quick, focused, and precise. However if someone becomes too yin they could be lethargic, weak or depressed, or if too yang tense, stiff or angry.

A skilled practitioner will use a variety of techniques to understand the cause of a problem and recommend the appropriate course of treatment. This will often include diet, exercise and lifestyle changes.

Simon Brown
Community Health Foundation
188 Old Street
London EC1V 98P
Tel: 071-251 4076

TRAGERWORK
PSYCHOPHYSICAL INTEGRATION

Milton Trager (1908–) discovered that gently and rhythmically rocking the body can connect into the unconscious and free up the mind/body. He first developed his work in response to victims of polio and other neuromuscular disorders, later applying it to physically normal people.

The approach emphasises sensitive adaptation to the individual to achieve release without discomfort, making it of special value in cases of painful restriction of movement or heightened vulnerability to pain. Clients are moved gently and nonintrusively through acceptable ranges of motion to communicate the experience of moving freely themselves.

Also included is instructions in Mentastics, a Trager-coined word referring to light, playful, mentally directed movements that are incorporated into everyday activities to enhance the effects of the tablework.

The Institute of Structural Bodywork
c/o Roger Golten, Synergy Centre
1 Cadogen Gardens, London SW3 2RJ

TRANSCENDENTAL MEDITATION

Transcendental Meditation (TM) is an easy to learn and highly effective way to combat the damaging effects of stress and to promote personal well-being. Revived by Maharishi Mahesh Yogi, the technique is many thousands of years old, yet has great relevance for the pace of life today.

Extensive scientific research in over 500 published studies has been conducted on TM and shows that it has a strong effect in reducing tension, anxiety, insomnia and overall levels of sickness. At the same time, it helps us to feel happier, think more clearly and be more positive about life in general.

TM is practised for 15–20 minutes twice per day and the technique itself feels relaxing and refreshing. It is always learned on a short course taught by a qualified teacher. To find out where you can learn TM and to receive more information free of charge simply telephone: 0800 269303, or write to:

Transcendental Meditation
FREEPOST, London SW1P 4YY

VEGETARIANISM

"With 7% of Britons now claiming to be vegetarian, the 'alternative' tag is no longer valid. Vegetarians eat no flesh, fish or fowl or slaughterhouse by-products because of disgust at present horrific factory farming methods and concern for the planet. To sustain our meat production, vast amounts of grain are imported from developing countries for animal feed while their people starve and rainforest is being destroyed at an alarming rate to provide cattle grazing land with disastrous implications for the greenhouse effect.

Medical opinion recognises the positive health benefits of a vegetarian diet. Containing well over the recommended requirements for protein and all essential vitamins and minerals, it is high in fibre and low in the saturated fats most commonly associated with animal foods. Consequently vegetarians cut their risk of heart disease by 30%. Studies show that diet-related illnesses such as kidney stones, diabetes, obesity and various forms of cancer are far less common amongst vegetarians. Meat accounts for 95% of all reported food poisoning cases.

The facts speak for themselves. Only a humane and holistic approach to diet will prevent massive human and animal suffering, protect our fragile environment and prevent many of the chronic diseases prevalent in Britain today."

Sean McElherron: Youth Education Manager
The Vegetarian Society
Parkdale
Dunham Road
Altrincham
Cheshire WA14 4QG

YOGA

Yoga is one of the oldest practises in the world. Basically it consists of a range of means by which men and women can appreciate the one-ness (Yoga) of life and find peace and health as a result. The means include physical movement carried out in a specific manner and various ways of concentrating the mind to encourage both calm thought and physical benefit. Yoga can be practised by followers of any religion or of none and will provide benefit in accordance to the seriousness with which it is followed.

Howard Kent: Director
The Yoga for Health Foundation, Ickwell Bury
Biggleswade, Beds. SG18 9EF
Tel: 0767 627271

YOGA has for centuries provided a system of physical and mental disciplines to improve strength, stamina, and flexibility, while calming the mind and relieving stress. Yoga promotes health and wellbeing, incorporates many methods, and appeals to all personalities and ages. Hatha Yoga is probably the most well known form and includes Asanas (body postures), Kriyas (cleansings), Pranayama (control of vital energy through breath-control), and Deep Relaxation to reduce stress and build self-confidence.

Hatha Yoga classes are widely available and often include Meditation to quieten the mind and improve concentration. Yoga can offer high impact exercise to appeal to the strong and healthy, or low impact techniques for the less able or those with special needs. Everyone works to their own ability and without the competitive element which is common to many other forms of exercise. Students attending their first class often report a surprising sense of wellbeing, when they expected to feel tired or stiff. This sense of wellbeing tends to increase with practise and is one of the reasons behind the growing popularity of Yoga.

To find a class near you, contact us at:

British Wheel of Yoga
1 Hamilton Place, Boston Road
Sleaford, Lincs NG34 7ES
Tel: 0529 306851

Iyengar Yoga Institute
223a Randolph Avenue, London W9 1NL
Tel: 071-624 3080

HERTFORDSHIRE

LANCASHIRE

LONDON

SURREY

YOGA

ZEN MEDITATION

Zen meditation is a form of Buddhist meditation
and therefore presupposes on the part of the
practitioner some knowledge of and desire to
practise that religion. In the initial stages of
learning to meditate, the purpose is to still the
mind. The techniques used to start this process
are the same in most Buddhist schools and consist
of concentrating on the act of breathing either
by counting the breaths or by observing each
inhalation and exhalation, most usually as they
pass the tip of the nose.

The Society publishes a Directory of Buddhist
groups, Centres and related organisations in the
United Kingdom and Ireland. It may be ordered
from the Society for £5.00 which includes postage
and packing.

The Buddhist Society
58 Ecclestone Square
London SW1V 1PH

British Buddhist Association
11 Biddulph Road, Maida Vale
London W9 1JA
Tel: 071-286 5575

HEALTH TESTING

THE FULL HEALTH CHECK

The Health Check is fully complementary to a
more traditional BUPA-type or GP check-up. It
also stands alone as a complete Preventive
Health Check. It tests for imbalances, stresses
and disturbances that are not covered in the
orthodox approach but which may be critical in
getting to the bottom of unusual or long-
entrenched symptom pictures or repetitive and
unwanted habits. It uses all the methods described
in the sheet called "Diagnostics". In the Health
Check we are looking in the main for environmental factors in disease that can be removed or
remedied. In particular the Health Check tests for
the following:

1) It establishes whether there are any allergies or
intolerances to particular foods, drugs, chemicals,
household or other substances, with instant
results.

2) It determines the way in which the body is
coming under stress and shows the organs that
are most affected.

3) It checks for mineral, vitamin, hormone and
enzyme deficiencies.

4) It gives a complete and thorough check on all
organs and functions and establishes any significant problems such as tumours, cancer, cystic
processes, intoxications, functional disturbances
or foci of infection.

5) It reveals the effect an illness is having in terms
of general deterioration and also the effect on
particular organs and functions, and it also shows
how well we are dealing with the illness i.e.
whether it is acute or chronic and whether there is
damage or not and if so whether it can be healed.
For previous illnesses it determines if they have
run their course or whether they are still present
but dormant or unresolved.

6) It reveals poisoning of the body by chemicals,
drugs, heavy metals (mercury, lead and cadmium), viruses, fungi, bacteria and other airborn,
waterborn or sexually transmitted toxins.

7) It reveals absorption problems in the digestive
system (dysbiosis) caused by an imbalanced
intestinal flora, including a candida (yeast) over-
growth that has spread from the bowel.

8) It reveals a predisposition to psychological and
emotional disorders and to depression.

9) It reveals a yin or yang imbalance, an acid or
alkaline imbalance, a cholesterol, protein, sugar,
carbohydrate or other nutritional overload, an
energy or meridian deficiency, a stressed chakra,
and a blockage of disturbance caused by scars
from previous injury or surgery.

10) It shows the presence of stress carried in the patient and caused by single or repeated exposures to harmful external factors (geopathic stress) such as distorted earth radiation at work or home, overhead power lines or electromagnetic stress from VDUs or other appliances, and it also detects radiation poisoning.

11) It shows the relative state of the immune system, whether there is a deficiency in immune function or an auto-immune disorder, and whether there is an excess or shortage of energy to respond to treatment.

12) It detects the presence of poisoning by substances from the chemical industry, from pesticides, food preservatives, solvents, and other environmental toxins, and of damage after antibiotics and other pharmaceuticals.

13) It shows, before using a herbal, homeopathic, mineral, vitamin or pharmaceutical medicine, to what extent it will be effective in balancing the patient's condition and whether it will be tolerated. It is therefore very helpful in planning the exact treatments that will produce the best possible results.

Following the Health Check I will advise on the best course of remedial treatment for an existing condition or the best preventive approach if there is no acute or chronic problem. This could include dietary adjustments, special exercises, home remedies, constitutional remedies or specific adjustments of daily habits. If treatment is called for I will plan a personal programme. This may include treatment here, referral to a specialist elsewhere in London or to a practitioner nearer to home. I may suggest acupuncture treatment, auricular treatment, Alexander lessons, counselling, osteopathy, shiatsu or other manipulation, colonics, herbalism, homoeopathy or further tests. If a patient has been referred by their GP or complementary practitioner I will send them a full report.

A full Health Check includes an examination of the irises of the eyes (iridology) either with a torch and lens, or with the iris microscope or by photography of the irises followed by analysis of the slides. This helps to place the patient's condition in relation to their ancestral heritage, particularly concerning genetic predispositions, inherited tendencies and levels of toxicity. It also helps in treatment planning and in the analysis of key mineral deficiencies.

Most of the testing, however, is done using the Vega machine to take readings from acupucture points on the feet or hands. The Full health Check takes two hours. This includes time for a full discussion of the findings and of future needs. It is painless, non-intrusive, stress-free, has instant results and no side-effects or after-effects.

John Morley
136 Harley Street, London W1N 1AH
Tel: 071-487 2617

COURSES: TUITION, WORKSHOPS, SEMINARS

COURSES: TUITION, WORKSHOPS, SEMINARS

COURSES: TUITION, WORKSHOPS, SEMINARS

LIFE Foundation School of Therapeutics (UK)

Centre for Health & Stress Management

HOLISTIC HEALTH CARE IN PRACTICE
Course providing essential information for Health Professionals and those interested in Holistic Healthcare.

DRU YOGA DIPLOMA COURSES
(Beginner to Advanced). Includes course book with tapes available.

HEALTH HOLIDAYS & RETREATS IN NORTH WALES AND BARDSEY ISLAND
Weekends and weeks to suit all ages, abilities and requirements.

NATIONAL & INTERNATIONAL YOGA & HEALTH TOURS
Workshops, Talks & Seminars from Gala to Chakra alignment and Stress Management.

4TH INTERNATIONAL YOGA CONFERENCE 1992
Books, Tapes, Leaflets.

STRESS MANAGEMENT CONSULTANCY
Courses & Consultancy to suit everybody's needs.

For further details and information on IYYH in your area and around the world. please contact L.F.S. (UK). c/o 15 Holyhead Road. Bangor. Gwynedd. North Wales LL57 2EG. Telephone: (Wales) 0248 370078 (Midlands) 0902 409164.

Pellin

3-year part-time Training Course in Gestalt Psychotherapy and Counselling for women and men. Courses begin January and October 1993.

Intensive Therapy Holidays in Agropoli, Southern Italy. July to September 1993.

PELLIN INSTITUTE

15 Killyon Road, London SW8 2XS

Telephone 071-720 4499

CO-COUNSELLING

Courses in North and Northwest London
Experienced Accredited Teacher (CCI)
Modest Charges. Open Introductory Evening, Plus free Courses for Unwaged.
BERNARD SPRINGER: 071-267 1560

The College of Natural Medicine, London

(the official establishment for the Association of GPs of Natural Medicine)

The College offers:

★ A Foundation Course in Comprehensive Natural medicine;

★ Post-graduate diploma and degree courses, starting 15 September each year.

Prospectus £2, from: Registrar, 38 Nigel House, Portpool Lane, London EC1N 7UR. Tel: 071-405 2781

PERSONAL DEVELOPMENT WORKSHOPS

Relaxation, Assertiveness
Stress-Management, Self Esteem

Contact:

Positive Steps Training
0782 311175

for a programme
(by experienced and qualified trainers)

Grampian School of Massage

Invite registrations from prospective students for our Basic Massage and Advanced Remedial Massage Courses

For further information and Brochure please contact:
Maggie Brooks or Nick Carter on 0224 822956
70 Lochside Road, Aberdeen

CRYSTAL COURSES
Certificated courses to a professional standard
Send for prospectus to:
The Secretary, Spiritual Venturers Association, 72 Pasture Road, Goole, North Humberside DN14 6HE
Telephone: (0405) 769119

COURSES: TUITION, WORKSHOPS, SEMINARS

COURSES: TUITION, WORKSHOPS, SEMINARS

COURSES: TUITION, WORKSHOPS, SEMINARS

ROSEMARY SCHOOL OF NATURAL THERAPY

The Principal:
Rosemary Frances Lockyer
Cert.Ed. (Sci. Biol.;, M.B.R.A., M.I.P.T.I., I.T.E.C.

- **Anatomy, Physiology & Massage**
- **Aromatherapy • Reflexology**
- **Sports Therapy • Nutrition/Diet**

ITEC Examination, Diplomas,
Small Groups, Individual attention.

10 Pine Ridge, Newbury, Berkshire RG13 2NQ
Tel: (0635) 31679

WENDY RIGBY SCHOOL OF NATURAL THERAPIES

COURSES LEADING TO ITEC EXAMINATIONS

Anatomy, Physiology and Massage
Aromatherapy
Reflexology

ITEC Registered School
**3 Ellerdale Road, Hampstead,
London NW3 6BA
Telephone: 071-435 5407**

Continuing Professional Development

OXFORD SCHOOL OF OSTEOPATHY

**TWO YEAR PART TIME DIPLOMA COURSE
IN OSTEOPATHY (D.O.)**

The Oxford School of Osteopathy offers mature, vocationally motivated students the opportunity to achieve a formal qualification in the rapidly expanding field of osteopathy.

Graduates will be eligible to apply for Membership of The Guild of osteopaths.

Admission to courses commencing in March 93 and March 94, based at the Department of Continuing Education, Rewley House, Oxford will be restricted to:

1. **State Resgistered Nurses.**
2. **State Registered/Chartered Physiotherapists.**
3. **Students with an appropriate qualification in an aligned subject e.g. physiology, remedial massage.**

Prospective students should apply to:
**The Principal, OSO, DOYLE Croft,
PO Box 67, Banbury OX16 8LE
Tel: (0869) 38353**

The London Tarot Training Centre

*21 Rosebery Gardens
Crouch End
London N8 8SH
081 340 3788*

COURSES: TUITION, WORKSHOPS, SEMINARS

MANCHESTER SCHOOL OF MASSAGE

Diploma Courses in Massage, Aromatherapy, Reflexology, Sports Therapy, on-site massage and Shiatsu. Weekday or Weekend Classes. Also Workshops available in Crystal Healing, Polarity, Bach Flower etc. Contact:
Manchester School of Massage, Freepost, Manchester M16 8HB or Telephone 061-862 9752

TWA ACRES NATURAL THERAPY CENTRE

THE TRAINING SCHOOL FOR THE PROFESSIONAL ASSOCIATION OF HYPNOTHERAPISTS(Scot)

Offers an three-part comprehensive Certificated Hypnotherapy Course which is designed to qualify students to practitioner level and to give them a thorough knowledge of Hypnotherapy/Hypnoanalysis with a sound practical training in induction methods and management of the hypnotic state through the application of Suggestion Therapy and Hypnoanalytical Techniques including Age Regression Methods. The course covers an eight week period the first two weeks of which are held in Blairgowrie during March, July and October.

For free prospectus contact:

TWA Acres Natural Therapy Centre
Woodlands Road, Blairgowrie PH10 6LD
Tel: 0250 874384 Fax: 0250 872879

THE PEARL HEALING CENTRE
Crystal and Colour Courses PHC
Sounds & Palmistry. Metamorphic Technique
Hypnotherapy
Healing by Appointment
Crystals, Gemstones, Books by Mail Order
37 Carew Road, Thornton Heath, Surrey CR7 7RF
Telephone 081 689 1771

British Astrological & Psychic Society
Booklet/Register of Consultants.
Basic Astrological Course, Meetings etc.
Send 90p stamps.
BAPS, 124 Trefoil Crescent, Broadfield, Crawley, Sussex RH11 9EZ

CLARENDON COLLEGE
PROFESSIONAL TRAINING COURSES IN
Facials · Electrolysis · Broken Veins · Body Massage · Aromatherapy · Waxing · Manic/Pedic (full & part-time)/ITEC Diploma.

515 HAGLEY ROAD, BRIMINGHAM, WEST MIDLANDS B66 4AX
Principal: Helen McElroy. Tel: 021 4299191

BRETFORTON HALL CLINIC

STUDENTS ACCEPTED FOR TRAINING IN CYMATIC THERAPY ARE ELIGIBLE FOR CAREER DEVELOPMENT LOANS.

ALL STUDENTS HAVING PASSED AND QUALIFIED ARE ALSO ELIGIBLE FOR AN INTERNATIONAL UNIVERSITY DEGREE.

ASK OR WRITE FOR DETAILS TO:
SECRETARY,
BRETFORTON HALL
SCIENTIFIC AND NATUROPATHIC
MEDICAL TRAINING
ESTABLISHMENT.
VALE OF EVESHAM.
WORCESTER WR11 5JH.
PHONE: 0386 830537

Hypnotherapy Training

under the auspices of the Association of Qualified Curative Hypnotherapists. Practical weekend courses commence each spring and autumn for those who have successfully passed the 3 month home-study section. Full details write or 'phone:
Therapy Training College, 8 & 10 Balaclava Road, Kings Heath, Birmingham B14 7SG. Tel: 021 444 5435

REFLEXOLOGY – COURSE/TUITION
REFLEXOLOGY COURSE LEADING TO A PROFESSIONAL QUALIFICATION. 9 MONTHS HOME-STUDY HOUR QUALIFIED HYPNOTHERAPIST, ACUPUNCTURIST, YOGA TUTOR, SHIATSU.
June A. Jackson, M.I.I.R., M.A.R., C.M.H.
40 Stratton Road, Brighouse HD6 3TA
Tel: 0484 719343

CLARIDGE HOUSE HEALING CENTRE
Dormansland, Lingfield, Surrey RH7 6QH.
Tel: (0342) 832150

Claridge House is a Quaker Centre where guests may stay for just a few days or for a few weeks. We offer **Healing, Massage** and **Counselling** throughout the year.
Excellent vegetarian food and the beautiful gardens afford a chance to unwind in an atmosphere of Peace.
From September through to next Easter we have Events and Workshops on a variety of subjects relating to Healing.
These include: **Massage; Circle Dancing; Using Meditation and Colour** for Self Healing & Inner Growth; Two linked weekends (parts 1 & 2) **Exploring Being a Channel for Healing; Use of Sound & Music in Healing; Medicine Wheel of North American Indians; Retreat Weekends; Personal medicine Crafts;** Weekends on **Exploring Past Lives; Elementals, Devas & Angels.** Please contact, if you wish to make a visit, or for more information on Workshops.

COURSES: TUITION, WORKSHOPS, SEMINARS

THE FACULTY OF ASTROLOGICAL STUDIES

TRAIN AT HOME

The Faculty is acknowledged by professional astrologers to be one of the best teaching bodies in the world. For over 40 years well known astrologers have trained on and taught its courses. Our correspondence school offers supportive tuition at all levels, and you can train to professional level by studying at home.

For further details ring:

071-700 3556
(24 hour answering)
or fax
071-700 6479
or write to:
**Dept. CS, FAS, BM7470,
London WC1N 3XX**

---

*THE NORTHERN ALLIED SCHOOL
OF REMEDIAL MASSAGE*
(Affiliated to The Northern Counties School of Osteopathy)

Part-time Course in Remedial Massage at Ushaw College, Durham - one weekend per month for two years. Theoretical and practical.

Full details from:
Robert Cuthbert, DO. MGO. Tel: 081-460 9386
Peter Ayton, DO. MGO. Cert.Ed. Tel: 0642 559690

AROMATHERAPY

ISPA Accredited

Massage & Reflexology

ITEC Diploma Courses
Quality training in small groups
**Berkshire School of Natural Therapy
21 Dukes Wood, Crowthorne,
RG11 6NF Crowthorne 0344 761715**

COLLEGE FOR SPORTS THERAPY & NATURAL MEDICINE

TRAINING IN NATURAL MEDICINE AND SPORTS THERAPY

Train for a new career as a therapist or acquaint yourself with the many therapies gaining new respect & credibility in the Nineties.
Fully accredited Diploma courses full and part time, weekend study, special Summer School programmes and introductory seminars.
- **NATURAL HEALTH PRACTITIONERS DIPLOMA**
- **MASTERS DIPLOMA IN SPORTS THERAPY**
- **DIPLOMA IN HOLISTIC AROMATHERAPY**
- **NUTRITION CONSULTANTS CERTIFICATE**
- **REFLEXOLOGY CERTIFICATE**
- **SWEDISH, HOLISTIC, THERAPEUTIC & SPORTS MASSAGE**
- **ACUPRESSURE & APPLIED KINESOLOGY**

Over 1500 therapists trained since 1983.
Prospectus ○ The Raworth Centre.
20- 26 South Street, Dorking, Surrey. RH4 2HG
Tel: 0306 742150

LOWER SHAW FARM
*Runs a full programme of weekend courses.
From seasonal celebrations, crafts and practical skills
to bodywork and the Spiritual.
Delicious Wholefood Vegetarian meals – Low costs.*
Full details **S.A.E. OLD SHAW LANE, SHAW, SWINDON, WILTSHIRE. 0793 771080**

Quest Designs & Promotions
WORKSHOPS, SEMINARS & CONCERTS
Chris James (Aus) – "**Transformation Through Sound**"
Evenings, weekends & 5 day residential
Tim Wheater – Mystic Flute, Sound & Music workshop and in concert
Kangaroo Moon – Inspiration from Australia in concert
Tarpan Alan Williams (Aus) – Massage/Dance/Music/Meditation workshops
Brochures, more details and cassettes, **0452 385848 Fax 0452 528294**

Lancashire Holistic College

I.T.E.C & I.F.A.
REGISTERED COURSES

* AROMATHERAPY
* HOLISTIC BODY MASSAGE
* BODY MASSAGE
* REFLEXOLOGY
* ANATOMY & PHYSIOLOGY

"Greenbank House', 65a Adelphi Street, Preston PR1 7BH
Tel: 0772 825177

COURSES: TUITION, WORKSHOPS, SEMINARS

HOME STUDY COURSES IN NATURAL MEDICINE

Diploma courses in Nutrition.
Homoeopathy, Herbal Medicine, Psychology,
Iridology, Reflexology, Auriculotherapy,
Massage, Aromatherapy,

No previous experience needed.

For prospectus please write sending postage stamp, or telephone:

INTERNATIONAL COLLEGE NATURAL HEALTH SCIENCES

NAME..

ADDRESS ....

....

.........................P/code...................

**2 Bath Place, Rivington Street,
London EC2A 3JJ.
Tel: 071-454 9988
Fax: 071-454 9980**

The *S.E.E.D.* Institute

10, Magnolia Way, Fleet,
Hants GU13 9JZ England
Tel/Fax: (0252) - 626448

Committed to Health & Vitality

TSI offers the following two-day, post-Graduate Courses:

* Aromatherapy & Learning Disabilities

In association with

* Aromatherapy and Public Speaking
* Aromatherapy, A.I.D.S. & H.I.V.
* Remedial/Sport-Injury Massage
* Aromatherapy and Ayurveda
* Aromatherapy & Children

AROMATHERAPY

PLUS: **Specialised two-day Courses:**

* Introduction to Aromatherapy   * Aromatherapy & Children
* Aromatherapy & Learning Disabilities   * Nutrition - (1-3)
* Advanced Remedial Massage   * Iridology - (1-3)
* Balanced Health (Kinesiology)   * Essence of Counselling
* Business Administration Workshop

Locations: **Hants., Northants., Herts., Leics., Scotland.**
(others considered for 10+ Participants)

Apply s.a.e. (large A4) to Courses Secretary, Ref 'A&C'

SELF-EXPLORATION - EDUCATION - DEVELOPMENT

TRADITIONAL HEALING COURSE
Together with a comprehensive part-time course on the science of healing

The Foundation of Traditional healing covers the integration of healing energies through theory and practise, creating a foundation for further studies, leading to a Diploma in Traditional healing.
For prospectus please write enclosing an SAE:
**Amethyst Healing Centre
Pink Roses, 1 Cree's Meadow,
Windlesham, Surrey GU20 6QA
or Tel: 0276-476811**

Proudfoot School of Hyponosis & Psychotherapy,
Proudfoot School, Blinking Sike, Eastfield Business Park, Scarborough YO11 3YT   **0723 363638**

Psychotherapy, Counselling, Hypnotherapy, Professional Diploma courses or study for interest, The National College, 12 Cross Street, Nelson, Lancs. BB9 7EN   **0282 699378**

T S K
(Time, Space and Knowledge)
A new vision of relativity.
Residential workshop in Dorset 22–27 May 1993
(£215)
Telephone: 0278 788624 (evenings)

CHELTENHAM THERAPY TRAINING CENTRE
The centre offers a complete range of courses from introductory workshops to professional practitioner training and post-graduate courses in:
THERAPEUTIC MASSAGE • AROMATHERAPY • REFLEXOLOGY SPORTS THERAPY
Small practical study groups to ensure a focus on individual tuition with attendance at weekends, mid-week days or evenings to suit your needs and other commitments.
For further information, prospectus and application form, please contact:
Valerie Johnston Deas, M.I.P.T.I., I.T.E.C., L.T.Phys.
*Norwood House 6 Lansdown Crescent Cheltenham
Gloucestershire GL50 2JY Tel: 0242 224283*
Registered with the International Therapy Examination Council.

COURSES: TUITION, WORKSHOPS, SEMINARS

Probably the Most Exciting Reflexology Course Available Today

The course offers a thorough and professional training in Reflexology
Anatomy and Physiology, Self Development, Bach Remedies, Deep Relaxation and Meditation

Philip Salmon School of Reflexology

Tel: 081-741 3255   Fax: 081-991 9714

The Dancing Wolf Initiative

Courses, weekend and residential workshops with Duncan Wordley. Medicine Wheel Teachings, Native American and Contemporary Shamanism, including the Dance work of Urban Shaman Gabrielle Roth.

Contact: **The Dancing Wolf Initiative**

126 Parc-Y-Dre, Ruthin, Clwyd LL15 1PH
Tel: 0824 702271

HYPNOTHERAPY AND NEURO-LINGUISTICS
The Caring Profession
Start A New Career
Add New Dimensions To Your Existing Profession

Fully residential Diploma courses at

DARTINGTON HALL, South Devon

Also running evening classes, video evenings, day and weekend seminars in Devon and Cornwall.

For **FREE** brochure
and syllabus:

The Harrisonian School
36 Lemon Street,
Truro, Cornwall
or telephone:
(0872) 77849
(24 hours)

HARRISONIAN SCHOOL
HYPNOSIS
— AND —
PSYCHOTHERAPY

White Rose School of Beauty & Therapies

We can prepare you for internationally recognised examinations in:
* Anatomy Physiology & Massage
* Anatomy & Physiology   * Diet & Nutrition
The above courses are available on a correspondence basis.
* Sports Therapy   * Aromatherapy
* Reflexology   * Aerobics teachers Diploma

Contact for a free prospectus:
The White Rose School Of Beauty
2nd Floor, Standard House,
George Street, Huddersfield HD1 4AD
Tel: (0484) 510625

POweR²

Power² Workshops
combine NLP,
you on video,
unique combinations
of concepts and
How To techniques.

The Power To . . .

LOVE THE CHILD WITHIN
LET GO OF GUILT
ASSERT YOURSELF
CREATE EMPOWERING RELATIONSHIPS

Details, please send a S.A.E. to:

Power²
37 Layfield Road
Hendon NW4 3UH

DIPLOMA IN NUTRITIONAL MEDICINE
Part-Time London In-Class Course of The Open-Study Course

The professional training leading to the diploma to practice, D.Th.D., and the higher grade practitioner's diploma D.N.Med., in wholistic Nutritional Medicine is by either *LONDON* attendance, one weekend per month or 24 months, commencing *OCTOBER* or the *OPEN-STUDY COURSE* commencing throughout the year.

THE COLLEGE OF NUTRITIONAL MEDICINE
(Offices: Devon & Greater Manchester)
PROSPECTUSES Tel: 0884 255059

PROSPECTUS & ALL ENQUIRIES
The College of Nutritional Medicine
Eastbank, New Church Road, Smithills
Greater Manchester BL1 5QP

LONDON IN-CLASS LOCATION
(Not for Prospectus Requests)
University of London
King's College, King's Road, Chelsea

COURSES: TUITION, WORKSHOPS, SEMINARS

BRITISH ASTROLOGICAL & PSYCHIC SOCIETY
Booklet/Register of Consultants.
Basic Astrological course. Meetings, etc.
Send 90p/Stamps.

**BAPS, 124 Trefoil Crescent, Broadfield, Crawley,
Sussex RH11 9EZ**

CRYSTAL COURSES
Certificated courses to a professional standard
Send for prospectus to:
**The Secretary, Spiritual Venturers Association,
72 Pasture Road, Goole,
North Humberside DN14 6HE
Telephone: (0405) 769119**

ALCHEMY OF ACCEPTANCE
WORKSHOPS WITH
PRATIBHA

With the help of dance, sound, breath, energy work, healing, crystals, aura soma, guided imagery, heart meditations, and much more, we will explore how life is transformed by the unconditional acceptance of ourselves in this moment.

Other courses: **Inner Man/Inner Woman
Journey through the chakras
Reiki I + II**
All enquiries: **071 582 1794**

The *S.E.E.D.* Institute
10, Magnolia Way, Fleet,
Hants GU13 9JZ England.
Tel/Fax: 0252 - 626448

Committed to the Unfoldment of the
TRUE SELF

Apply s.a.e. (A4) for Overview of Self-Development Workshops, Home-Studies and Audio-Cassettes, incorporating Hemi-Sync*, and continuous Mental Development Courses - quoting reference 'A&C3'

* Hemi-Sync is a TM of The Monroe Institute, Va. U.S.A.

SELF - EXPLORATION - EDUCATION - DEVELOPMENT

HEALTH CENTRES/CLINICS/PRACTITIONERS

BERKSHIRE

Natural Healing Counselling
Community Centre, Farnham Road, Slough
Telephone: 0753 674014
Qualified Practitioners who love you!

DEVON

THE CLINIC
**37 St Peter Street
Tiverton
Devon EX16 6NW**

★ Aromatherapy ★ Allergy Testing
★ Constructive Living Instructor
★ Homoeopathy ★ Hypnotherapy ★ Psychotherapy
★ Remedial and Therapeutic Massage
★ Acupuncture

For appointments or further information please ring
Tiverton (0884) 255990
8.30am–6.00pm Monday–Friday

ESSEX

Revd. Dr Vernon Bell, B.Sc., M.Sc., Ph.D., D.D.
Centrepast lives regression therapy/research/reincarnation (registered). Novice trainee groups. Also one to one hypnotic regression therapy. Psychosomatic problems.
**95 Prospect Road, Woodford Green, Essex
Tel: 081-505 8720**

THE TRINITY CENTRE
The centre is concerned with the health and wellbeing of the whole person (to this end we offer therapies and activities which will foster healing personal growth and spiritual awareness.)

Therapies available at the centre:
Acupuncture, Alexander Technique, Aromatherapy, Bach Flower Remedies, Biofeedback, Chinese Herbal Medicine, Counselling, Healing, Homoeopathy, Reflexology.
Also we have a comprehensive library and offer a full programme of workshops.

**12 & 21 Trinity St.
Colchester
0606 561150**

HEALTH CENTRES/CLINICS/PRACTITIONERS

ESSEX

GREAT CLACTON NATURAL HEALING CENTRE

★ Homoepathy ★ Reflexology
★ Metamorphic Technique ★
Shiatsu ★ Chiropody ★ Aromatherapy
★ Graphology ★ Counselling
★ Slimming Consultants ★ Healing ★

For more information or appointments please phone

0255 436059

in confidence. We are here to help you in whatever way we can.

6 St. Johns Road, Great Clacton, Essex

LIFE-FORCE
CENTRE FOR NATURAL WELL-BEING

COUNSELLING, PSYCHOTHERAPY,
HOMOEOPATHY, REFLEXOLOGY,
HYPNOTHERAPY, HYPNOHEALING,
HYPNOANALYSIS, REBIRTHING,
REIKI HEALING.

Courses in:
Assertiveness
Stress Management
P.E.T.
(Parents Effective Training)

Regular Group:
The Alternative Friday Group
Art Therapy, Drama, Psychodrama,
Movement and Self Awareness.
SPEND YOUR FRIDAYS
IN A DIFFERENT WAY!

TEL: 0206 250071

GREATER MANCHESTER

CHEADLE HULME NATURAL HEALTHCARE CENTRE & SPORTS INJURY CLINIC
Now offers:
Hypnotherapy, Reflexology, Stress Management,
Therapeutic Massage, Aromatherapy and Sports Injuries.
One day workshops and courses now available.
23 Mellor Road, Cheadle Hulme, Cheshire.
Telephone: 061-485 4009

WEST GLAMORGAN

the heyokah centre
FOR HEALING ARTS & CRAFTS
Books, Crystals, Oils,
Candles, Native American Crafts

wide range of healing therapies
Tai Chi, Chi Kung, Reiki, Counselling
Floatation Room
Visit us for Lunch

2 Humphrey Street, Swansea
(0792) 457880

HAMPSHIRE

The Bridge Street Clinic
11 Bridge Street, Winchester
Tel: 0962 853260
Established over 20 years in the practice of Natural medicine.
OSTEOPATHY. MEDICAL HERBALISM. HOMOEOPATHY.

THE SOUTHSEA CENTRE FOR COMPLEMENTARY MEDICINE
Acupuncture ● Homoeopathy ● Hypnotherapy
Jin Shin Jyutsu ● Osteopathy
25 Osborne Road, Southsea, Hampshire PO5 3ND
Tel: 0705 874748

KENT

NATURAL MEDICINE CENTRE
87 Beckenham Lane, Shortlands, Bromley, Kent BR2 0DN. Tel: 081-460 1117
Acupuncture, Aromatherapy, Homoeopathy,
Psychotherapy, Reflexology, Shiatsu
BOOKS – TAPES – REMEDIES – CRYSTALS

LONDON

Aromatherapy, Holistic massage and counselling,
Yoga classes – all levels plus childrens and ante-natal
yoga groups. Wide variety of courses/workshops/products.
Wheelchair access throughout.

Swanfleet Centre
93 Fortress Road, London NW5 1AG
Tel: 071-267 6717

London   Highgate N6
JILL R. HYAMS, M.B.A.L.C.T.
Holistic Body Therapist
Nutritional therapy, allergy testing, Candida,
Psychological problems, applied kinesiology,
Shiatsu body massage.
For appointments ring: 081-340 8934. 9am–6pm.

HEALTH CENTRES/CLINICS/PRACTITIONERS

LONDON

The Highbury Centre, Refia Sacks and Alan Mars, 137 Grosvenor Ave., London N5 2NH **071-226 5805**

ALL HALLOWS HOUSE, CENTRE FOR NATURAL HEALTH AND COUNSELLING
Idol Lane, London EC3   Tel: 071-283 8908
18 complementary therapies offered by top practitioners who work as a team. Not sure which therapy? or what is wrong? Ring for advice or book an initial consultation for an holistic examination and individual advice. £12.

Violet Hill Studios
CENTRE FOR
CREATIVE HEALING
Spacious Consulting Rooms, a Conference Suite and Art Studios sensitively restored from an Eighteen Century Barn
6 Violet Hill, St John's Wood, London NW8 9EB
Tel: 071-624 6101/071-624 0101/081-458 5368

NEW CROSS NATURAL THERAPY CENTRE
We offer a wide range of therapies including:
Acupuncture, Homoeopathy, Psychotherapy, Gestalt, Shiatsu, Osteopathy, McTimoney Chiropractic, Ortho-Bionomy, Cranio-Sacral, Alexander Technique, Aromatherapy, Massage
394 New Cross Road, London SE14 6TY
Tel: 081-469 0858

HELIOS CENTRE
Tel: 071-713 7120
A centre for New Opportunities. 2 mins from Kings Cross Station. Groups + Workshops + Classes + Holistic practices. Aromatherapy Iridology, Osteopathy, Psychosynthesis, Reflexogy, Shiatsu, Yoga etc.

The Hampstead Rooms
North London's newest venue for holistic courses and private therapy. Centrally located with very affordable rates.
126 Finchley Road
071-431 8169

John Morley
M.A., B.Ac., M.T.Ac.S., M.A.A., R.Ir., M.Soc. Biol. Med.
Preventive Medicine, Regeneration, Environmental and Full Health Checks
136 Harley Street, London W1N 1AH
For details please write or phone:
071-487 2617

Dr David L. S. Paine,
M.B., Ch.B., M.R.C.G.P., Dip.Ac.(Beijing), M.F.Hom.
For Acupuncture and Homoeopathy please contact:
London Medical Centre	The Consulting Rooms
144 Harley Street	Orchard Paddock
London	Bugbrooke
W1N 1AH	Northampton NN7 3QR
071-935 0023	0604 832256

Nigel Gray, Body centred, Holistic Psychotherapist, London N7 based **071-607 1823**

THE GERDA BOYESEN CENTRE
BIODYNAMIC PSYCHOLOGY AND MASSAGE
A natural approach to deep relaxation
Individual treatments by graduate therapists.
Complete training courses. Short courses.
Acacia House, Centre Avenue,
Acton Park, London W3 7JX
Tel: 081 746 0499

LOTHIAN

EDINBURGH HOLISTIC HEALTH CENTRE
We have a wide range of therapies available including: Acupressure, Aromatherapy, Acupuncture, Counselling, Homoeopathy, Hypnosis, Massage, Osteopathy, Shen, Stress Management. We are open Mon–Fri 9am–7.30pm.
26a Inverleith Row, Edinburgh EH3 5QH.
Tel: 031-551 5091

MIDDLESEX

HARROW   WEMBLEY/ST. ALBANS
NATURAL HEALTH CLINIC
T. H. JIVRAJ B.Sc.(Hons), D.Hom.(Med.), Acupressure.
Postal service allergy testing/treatment by sending a hair sample for full test by radiesthesia only £15.00.
Homoeopathy · Nutrition · Allergy T/T · Autogenic Training · Bates Method · Alexander Technique · Acupressure without needle · Candida · Me
Allergy Clinic   Appointment: 081-908 4272
286 Preston Rd, Harrow,   081-907 5357
Middlesex   0727-923298

NEWCASTLE UPON TYNE

NATURAL HEALTH CENTRE
Natural healing counselling, Dowsing, Bach-flower remedies. Positive thinking. Treatment by appointment only. First consultation FREE
★ Relaxation cassettes – CD's and Vidjeos for sale ★
Courses, Seminars and Workshops also available.

Noel G. Sorbye, Natural healer
N.F.S.H., B.H.M.A., N.M.S., S.M.N.
The Natural Health Centre
Talbot House, 17 The Bigg Market
Newcastle upon Tyne NE1 1UN
Tel: 091-261 9483 (24 hrs)

NORTHAMPTON

Dr. D. Paine for Acupuncture & Homoeopathy.   0604 832256
or 071-935 0023

HEALTH CENTRES/CLINICS/PRACTITIONERS

OXFORDSHIRE

THE ALISTER HARDY RESEARCH CENTRE
for the Study of Spiritual and Religious Experience
The AHRC invites accounts of spiritual transcendent or
religious experience. Membership Scheme, News Letters,
Lectures and Events. For further information write to:
The Alister Hardy Research Centre (D)
Westminster College, Oxford OX2 9AT, or Tel: 0865 243006

SOMERSET

Mano Warren, M.Rx.S., I.T.E.C., Reflexology, Holistic
Massage   0749-670746

COMPLEMENTARY MEDICINE SERVICES
(incorporating the Allergy Centre)

**9 CORPORATION STREET
TAUNTON, SOMERSET TA1 4AJ
Tel: 0823 325022   Fax: 0823 325024**

Do you need help with recurrent
health problems?
*Candida (thrush) Cystitis,
Irritable bowel, Allergies, Fluid retention,
Hyperactivity (children), Stress, Migraine,
Pre-menstrual Symptoms.*
Come and talk to us . . . we are right
next to the Library.
We are also at the Redgate Medical Centre,
Westonzoyland Road, Bridgwater.
Tel: 0278 444411

Our practitioners are fully qualified, and they
are always happy to spend 10 minutes
discussing a particular problem with you
prior to making an appointment.

*Acupuncture · Aromatherapy · Chiropody · Colonic Hydrotherapy
Dietary Therapy · Food Allergy Testing · Herbal Medicine
Holistic Massage · Hypnotherapy · Homoeopathy – Iridology
Osteopathy · Psychotherapy · Reflexology · Shiatsu
Vitamin & Mineral Deficiency Testing*

STAFFORDSHIRE

Leek Natural Therapy Centre
Physiotherapy/Reflexology: **Mrs L. Skellam,**
M.C.S.P.(S.R.P.) 0538 383726
Homoeopathy: **Mrs J. Povey,**
B.Sc.(Hons), L.N.W.C.H., R.S.Hom. 0538 385346
Remedial Massage: **Mrs E. Rybak-Coare,**
L.C.S.P.(Assoc.) 0538 360999

STRATHCLYDE

Cadzow Clinic   0698 283653

SUFFOLK

Brandon Natural Health Clinic, Reflexology, Osteopathy,
Acupuncture, Homoeopathy, Dietary Therapy,   **0842 811222**
or **0842 813514**

Brandon Natural Health Clinic,
9 Bury Road, Brandon, Suffolk IP27 0BU   **0842 811222**

SURREY

ANDREW GALBRAITH, M.F.Phys., M.I.S.P.A., M.S.R.Hom.
KAY GALBRAITH, M.F.Phys., M.I.S.P.A., M.S.R.Hom.
Natural Health Practitioners
Aromatherapy · Bach Flowers · Massage in Pregnancy · Nutrition
Mineral Therapy · Therapeutic Massage
Radionic Homoeopathy · Reflexology
Kingston upon Thames 081-546 0290

ROBERT MONTEZ, D.O., M.G.O., M.I.P.H.
Osteopath, Naturopath, Homoeopath.
**Brabant House Clinic, Portsmouth Road,
Thames Ditton, Surrey KT7 0EY
1 Ashley Drive, Ashley Park, Walton-on-Thames,
Surrey KT12 1JL
Tel: 081-3987592 / 0932 254 630**

FARNHAM HOLISTIC CENTRE

Support your Local Charity.
Registered Charity No. 295088

Providing: Acupuncture, Aromatherapy, Bach
and Bailey Flower Remedies, Counselling,
Electro-Crystal Healing, Healing, Hypnotherapy,
Massage, Meditation, Osteopathy, Psychotherapy,
Reflexology, Shiatsu and Stress Management.

**Tilford Road, Farnham, Surrey GU9 8HU.
Tel: 0252 734445**

SUSSEX

FLINT HOUSE
Natural Health Clinic and Learning Centre
Daily treatments in a wide range of natural therapies.
Weekend workshops run by inspiring leaders.
Beneficial day and evening courses.
We would welcome a visit at
41 High Street, Lewes
(entrance in St. Nicholas Lane) or please
Telephone: (0273) 473388

HEALTH CENTRES/CLINICS/PRACTITIONERS

EAST SUSSEX

THE COTTAGE CLINIC
R. THURSTAN, D.M.O., M.Phy.A., M.B.E.O.A.
OSTEOPATHY ● PHYSIOTHERAPY
SOFT LASER LIGHT THERAPY

Bexhill-on-Sea (0424) 222070
25 Sea Road, Bexhill-on-Sea, E. Sussex TN40 1EE

WEST SUSSEX

Acorn Centre for Natural Health, Natural Health Clinic & Meeting
Hall, 57a Railway Approach, East Grinstead RH19 1BT   0342 317620

WILTSHIRE

ASHTANGA CENTRE
for
COMPLIMENTARY MEDICINE
Established in 1982. The Centre in addition to running training courses on **KINESIOLOGY, MASSAGE (ITEC) AND HYPNOSIS,** conducts a daily surgery in Trowbridge offering a wide range of therapies incl:
● **ALLERGY TESTING**
● **HYPNOSIS**
● **TOUCH FOR HEALTH (KINESIOLOGY)**
● **REFLEXOLOGY**
● **COUNSELLING (ONE TO ONE)**
The Centre also has for sale deep relaxation tapes to boost confidence and reduce stress. Also its very successful book bringing relief to arthritis suffers.
For a Private Confidential Consultation:
Telephone 0985 40659

HEALTH RETREATS/HOLIDAYS

Hatha Yoga Holidays, Mrs J. Lavers, 33 Percy Road,
Pocklington, York YO4 2LZ   0759 304140
See our Advertisement under Yoga

CORNWALL

Personalised Programmes, Healing – Shiatsu for stress,
self-discovery, life balance.   Brochure 0736 731126

CUMBRIA

Crosthwaite
★ Mill ★
LAKE DISTRICT – LYTH VALLEY
The perfect retreat. Our water mill is a very special place to be at peace with the world and oneself. Simply enjoy the atmosphere, the countryside and the delicious vegetarian meals, or come to one of our varied courses, music recitals and other events in this inspirational setting.
Please write or phone for details:
Angela and John Pogson, Crosthwaite Mill,
Nr. Kendal, Cumbria   (05395) 68314

DEVON

Hazelwood House
Beautiful River Valley
Bed and Breakfast, Good Organic Food, Pure Water, Cottages,
Special care for the weary and convalescent, Open all year.
Cultural events and courses
0548 82 232 / 081 883 2124

Yeo Cottage
Breaks for Peace, Relaxation, Healing, Spiritual Counselling
and your Thatched Cottage, 2 miles Totnes.
Michael Cox, Yeo Cottage,
Sandwell Lane, Totnes, Devon
Tel: 0803 868157

HIGHLANDS

Jenny's Bothy
Small, simple, secluded in Eastern Cairngorms, ideal for family
holidays, small groups, courses.
S.A.E. Jenny Smith
Dellachuper, Corgarff, Strathdon, Aberdeenshire AB36 8YP.
Ring **Michelle Scrimgeour**   **09756 51446**

SOMERSET

EXMOOR PEACE
The Pack Horse, Allerford, Nr. Minehead
Therapeutic leylines cross our holiday homes. Come and share their
healing energies. Ample parking. Beautiful countryside. Holistic massage
and Reiki healing available. For brochure write or ring:
0643 862475
Open all year.

SPAIN

Spain – *Cortijo Romero,*
creative Holiday courses in the sun drenched foothills of the
Sierra Nevada. Vegetarian food and swimming pool.
Open March–November. **1993 Brochure out NOW!** *contact:*
Wendy, 24 Grange Avenue, Chapeltown, Leeds LS7 4EJ.
Tel: **0532 374015.**

HEALTH RETREATS/ HOLIDAYS

WEST SUFFOLK

SUNRISE RETREAT IN WEST SUFFOLK

Weekend gatherings, workshops support groups – camps. Also private rebirthing and Reiki healing – **Mary Ethelwood**, B.R.S.

19th–21st March – Spring Equinox
9th–12th April Easter – Water Rebirthing
23rd–25th April – 1st Degree Reiki Training
30th April–3rd May – Beltaine Camp
28th–31st May – Whitsun Camp
2nd–4th July – Full Moon Camp
August Bank Holiday 27th–30th – Weekend Camp
19th, 20th, 21st September – Autumn Equinox
29th, 30th, 31st October – Samhain

Mary Ethelwood 0359 221276

WALES

Cerridwen, Purpose-built centre for courses/workshops, sleeps 16+, Penybanc Farm, Velindre, Llandysul, Dyfed **0559 370 211**

Real Lighthouse on crossing leylines

Grade II Listed, with superb B&B accommodation, floatation tank and W. Reich's orgone accumulator.
Just the place to unwind and deeply relax
Tel: (0633) 810126/815860

WORCESTERSHIRE

MALVERN NATURE CURE CENTRE
* Set in the lovely Malvern hills for quiet holidays of invigorating walks. Attractive well appointed bedrooms.
* Suitable for vegetarian guest or patients. Superb vegetarian cuisine.
* Full range of Nature Cure therapies from experienced staff including massage manipulation, relaxation, exercise, individually prescribed diets and psychotherapy.
* Write enclosing SAE or telephone for brochure, tariff and free guide to Malvern.

Registered Naturopaths
Michael Forman and Margaret Golding,
5 College Grove, Great Malvern, Worcs. WR14 3HP.
Tel: Malvern 0684 566818

PRODUCTS/SERVICES

BOOKS

Genesis Books
Body – Mind – Spirit – Environment
10% discount in 1993 on first orders for new Mail-Order Customers

188 Old Street   Phone 071-250 1868
London EC1V 9FR   Fax 071-490 3049

Visionary Designs, P.O. Box 1177, Brighton BN1 1RX **0566 85243**
Fax: **0566 85540**

Arista Holistic Centre
Books Metaphysical and Esoteric. Unit N & M,
Royal Albert Walk, Albert Road, Southsea, Hants. PO4 0JT.
Telephone: 0705 293668/0705 824493
Open 10am–5.30pm Mon–Sat.

CONSULTANT MEDIUM

Mark Alexander, London/Gloucester, Spiritual Intuitive Aura/ Tarot/Sacred Path consultations. Extraterrestrial interdimensional communication **0452 385848**

CRYSTALS

CRYSTALS
Hand Carved Rose quartz Dolphins, spheres, eggs, pendants, crystal jewellery, Natural and Cut Gemstones.
P. C. Santos
79 Randolph Avenue, London W9 1DW
Tel: 071 286 2081 Fax: 071 266 2555

DIETICIAN

H. Simpson, D.O.-N.C.S.O., M.G.O.(Lon.), M.I.C.A.K., M.R.S.H., M.H.P.A., M.A.A., M.C.K.O.R.E. **0744 88 3737**

EAR CANDLES

EAR CANDLES BUAV APPVD PRODUCTS
* HOPI INDIAN REMEDY, used for sinusitis, tinnitus headaches and stress and most ENT problems.
* CELL ENERGY CREAMS, an edible all natural product for skin disorders, cellulite, strains, tensions, rejuvenates and softens skin.
* HIGH ENERGY PIEZO electric therapy system, no batteries or mains, used for needle-less acupuncture, physiotherapy, rheumatism, arthritis, sports injuries. 14 day free trial.

Tel: 0621 88411
Sheepcoates Lane,
Great Totham,
Maldon, Essex
CM9 8NT

UK Ltd

Sole UK Importers for full Biosun range

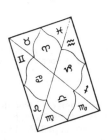

PRODUCTS/SERVICES

HEALTH & BEAUTY

100% Natural. Over 1,000 different herbs.
Treats: Arthritic, Rheumatic, Mouth, Skin & Internal conditions
Sandy Rodgers, I.T.E.C. Massage
Grove House, Belchamp Walter, Sudbury CO10 7AR
Tel: 0787 313413

HEALTH STORE

TALK TO THE EXPERTS!
We specialise in ★ Natural medicines ★ Nutritional supplements ★ Cruelty-free cosmetics ★ Crystals ★ Vegetarian & Wholefoods ★ Books ★ Herbal Teas ★ Green Products ★ Allergy-free foods ● All you expect in a good Health Store and more!
Trained staff, always willing to give FREE help and advice.
Member of the National Association of Health Stores
Great Clacton Health Store, 6 St. Johns Road, Great Clacton, Essex
Tel: 0255 436059
Also: All Natural, 27 Pier Avenue, Clacton-on-Sea, Essex. Tel: 0255 435629

HEALING PRODUCTS

TIGER RUGS · SILK & WOOL MEDITATION SHAWLS · ANTIQUE DANCERS' MASKS

WOODEN PHURPAS · ANTIQUE DORJEES & BELLS · POTTERY

OLD TEXTILES · PRAYER WHEELS · BRONZE FIGURES · DRUMS

SINGING BOWLS SHAMANIC AND BUDDHIST RITUAL IMPLEMENTS
We have been supplying healers, therapists and teachers for over 12 years.
For details of mail order send A5 SAE

ALAIN ROUVEURE
TIBETAN RUGS, HIMALAYAN TEXTILES AND TRIBAL ART
CROSSING COTTAGE GALLERIES
TODENHAM, NR. MORETON-IN-MARSH, GLOS GL56 9NU
TEL 0608 50418
OPEN FRI , SAT, SUN AND BANK HOLIDAYS
FROM 10AM TO 5PM – OTHER TIMES BY APPOINTMENT

TIBETAN BELLS & CYMBALS · TRIBAL JEWELLERY · GONGS · THANGKA PAINTINGS

HOMOEOPATHIC PRODUCTS

OPTIMUM–PHOENIX
Main Mail Order Suppliers

DR RECKEWEG'S

COMPLEX HOMOEOPATHIC REMEDIES,
AROMATHERAPY COSMETICS, VETERINARY, HERBS,
TINCTURES, OILS BOOKS

20%off   1st order

FREE BROCHURE
TEL: 0398 332000

IMPACT THERAPY

Enrico Dodson, L.C.S.P.(Assoc.), M.I.I.R., M.B.S.A.M.,
21 Cowlersley Lane, Huddersfield HD4 5TY   0484 641982

MAIL ORDER

Neti Pots for salt-water nasal cleansing. Hand-thrown ash-glaze stoneware, £6.50 plus £2 p&p.
Joan Smith,
'Stream Cottage' 21 Downview Ave.,
Ferring, West West Sussex BN12 6QN.

NATURAL HEALING FROM THE APOTHECARY
Dried Herbs, Tinctures, Aromatherapy Products, Flower, Gem and Environmental Essences (Alaskan, Australian Bush, Bach, Californian, Pegasus, Perelandra), Celtic and Devic healing Oils, Homoeopathic Remedies, Nutritional Supplements, Toiletries, Books, Tapes, Posters and more.

Send £1 for catalogue, redeemable with first order to:

Phoenix Apothecary, Findhorn Foundation, The Park, Findhorn Bay, Forres, Moray IV36 0TZ. Tel: 0309 691044. Fax: 0309 690933

Spirit Guide
The new name in "New Age" mail order.
Your requirements are our business.
We now stock New Age tapes and have a new tape, exclusive to Spirit Guide, by Arny Sage.
We also have Aromatherapy oils, Incense sticks and oils.
Our extensive Tarot card and book list is second to none.
See our wide range of Austrian PRISM Crystal pendants.
We have a broad range of individual gemstones to suit your needs as well as gemstone collections for special problems.
We stock the WELLBEING pouches created by Kertta.
Send 28p stamp for mail order catalogue, normal cost 60p, to:
**Spirit Guide, 199 Dialstone Lane,
Stockport SK2 7LF
Tel/Fax: 061-483 3846 (B. Kerr Proprietor)**

PHOENIX RISING
BRINGING YOU THE BEST IN NEW AGE SUPPLIES
CRYSTALS, CARDS, BOOKS, TAPES, BOJI STONE, MAYAN CHIMES, AROMATHERAPY OILS AND MUCH MORE
For Mail order catalogue and workshop information:
Tel: 0787 371798 or Fax: 0787 376667

NEW AGE PRODUCTS

BODY AND SOUL
**87a High Street
Great Missenden,
Bucks. HP16 0AL**

★ Books ★ Relaxation Tapes ★
★ Silver Jewellery ★ Crystals ★
★ Incense ★ Essential Oils ★
★ Development Courses ★ Mail Order ★

**Open 9.30–6.00 Monday – Saturday
Tel: 0494 891669**

Mysteries
Loudon's Psychic Shop and new Age Centre
Tarot Cards, Pendulums, Crystals etc.
Thousands of books on all related subjects: from Acupuncture to Rebirthing to Zen etc.
Also **Resident Psychic Readers** – Tarot, Palm, Crystal, Astrology, etc.
(Appointments not always necessary)
9 Monmouth Street WC2 (071 240 3688)

PRODUCTS/SERVICES

NEW AGE PRODUCTS

Wholesale distributors and Manufacturers of a comprehensive range of natural and organic products.

WE OFFER

★ Wholefood cash and carry to the trade
★ A regular delivery service
★ Competitive prices

Phone now for more information and helpful advice, on Bristol (0272) 583550 or write to Unit 3, Lodge Causeway Trading Estate, Fishponds, Bristol BS16 3JB.

PERSONAL TAPES

INNER VISIONS
Personally prepared by
DARRYL O'KEEFFE
exclusively for you
Tel: 071-607 2367

PRINTS

PUBLICATIONS

Berrydales Special Diet News
an information packed quarterly magazine for anyone interested in special diets and healthy eating.
Call 071 722 2886 (Fax: 072 722 7685) for more details.

RELATIONSHIPS

Clearing negative thought patterns. Cutting the ties that bind. Clearing physical and emotional energy blocks. Looking at relationships and their Karmic connection.

Sharon Jarvis works with individuals and groups, helping them improve the way they communicate and perceive life's lessons.

Sharon Jarvis
3 Thornwood, Mile End, Colchester
Essex CO4 5LR. Tel: 0206 854407

TREATMENT COUCHES

Is Your Table Heavy?
Does it Wobble and Squeak?
Was It Expensive?
Then You Don't Have
A ROCK SOLID TABLE!
Don't make a mistake before you decide.
Call the information line now.
081 577 2877

new concept
TREATMENT COUCHES

★ Custom made couches to the highest standards of workmanship and design
★ Adjustable height PROFESSIONAL couch available
★ Options of face hole, insert and lifting back rest
★ Accessories hand made in natural fabrics
★ Couches and accessories colour co-ordinated in a range of pastel shades
★ Together with our established range of products we would like to introduce you to our new 'Companion' massage chair and 'Colleague' (desk top version) which provide the opportunity for massage therapists to extend their repertoire to include revitalising seated massage in offices, factories, health clubs, shopping centres, beauty salons and a host of other locations

For further details contact
New Concept, Dept CHG, Cox Hall Lane,
Tattingstone, Ipswich IP9 2NS.
Tel/Fax No: 0473 328006

YOGA PRODUCTS

Surrey Iyengar Yoga Centre, Church Farm House, Spring Close Lane, Cheam, Surrey SM3 8PU. "Physical exercise brings back a state of Joy & Harmony" 081-6440309